Rhona Cullinan
with The Irish
Academy of Beauty

LOOK
GOOD
FEEL
GOOD

A step-by-step makeup
book to give you new
confidence

First published in Ireland in 2009 by Irish Academy of Beauty.

Layout, Design & Editing: mOuLd Design

Photography: Beta Bajgartova

British Library Cataloguing in Publication Data
A catalogue record of this book is available from the British Library

ISBN 978-0-9562108-0-7

Disclaimer:
The author and publishers have made every effort to ensure that the information in this book was accurate at the time of going to press, and accept no responsiblity for any injury or inconvenience sustained by any person using this book or following the advice provided herein.

CONTENTS

I am delighted to provide this introduction to "Look Good Feel Good". All of us involved with the Marie Keating Foundation are incredibly aware of the dedicated Support provided to those living with breast cancer, a disease that sadly continues to touch the lives of far too many of us.

Since my mother died in 1998 the increased knowledge and awareness that people now have amazes me. Women used to suffer alone, but now doors have been opened so those who face a breast cancer diagnosis have greatly improved treatment options and a better quality of life. They also have a vast and growing support network including specialist Cancer Support nurses.

I do a lot of travelling and have the privilege of meeting women who are either touched by cancer personally or who are responding to the life-saving message of early detection. I can assure you that people are embracing the spirit of the breast cancer cause throughout the world more than ever before.
My congratulations to you on your book "Look Good Feel Good". I hope this book will provide help and support to those who read it.

Take Care

Marie Keating
FOUNDATION

Following the death of their mother, Marie, in 1998 each member of the Keating family promised that they would do everything they could to bring an end to breast cancer. They committed to provide all women and their families with the necessary information to prevent cancer or detect it at its earliest stages. Their collective aim was to "Making Cancer Less Frightening by Enlightening". The Marie Keating Foundation is the realisation of a family's dedication - it is a promise to themselves, in action.

To achieve this we:

- Increase awareness and knowledge on cancer and issues related to it to all sectors of the community.
- Promote early detection and treatment.
- Provide support services to those affected by cancer where identified gaps exist.
- Work closely with various cancer-related groups and organisations to complement and optimise efforts to eradicate cancer as a life threatening disease.

We focus on cancers that can be prevented through lifestyle changes and early detection and our ultimate goal is a future free from the fear of cancer.

Introduction

I began my career in makeup over 15 years ago and have gained extensive experience in every area of the industry from fashion, catwalk, editorial, television to brides getting made up for their big day. I most recently began working with a specialised voluntary program called "Look Good Feel Better" where we go to the cancer patients in hospitals around the country showing them how to use makeup and feel better about themselves. My passion for makeup has always been about seeing the smile on a woman's face when she looks in the mirror after being made up.

I met Derek O'Kelly (Director of The Irish Academy of Beauty) when I began teaching makeup courses there. Having been appointed head of the makeup department we began developing both basic and advanced courses to teach up and coming makeup artists the best techniques I had learned along the way. Derek then asked me to help with developing an instructional DVD for make-up for our students which was very successful. Following on from this we decided to write an instructional guide to make-up. The idea for the guide developed into a book, which we also agreed would help with another interest we had in common; raising funds for charities. We decided that proceeds from the book would be donated to a charity and set about finding an organisation that would support our efforts. Following several weeks of research, we contacted the Marie Keating Foundation, an organisation that is committed to the fight against breast cancer.

Our first meeting with Linda Keating, director of fundraising, was inspirational. She thought the book was a great idea and would fully support our efforts. She explained of her experiences with cancer patients and how make-up could lift their mood. In fact our meeting with Linda helped shape the book. It encouraged us to produce a book that would demonstrate how make-up was not just an image enhancing solution, but could also be used to enhance self esteem. The meeting also encouraged us to use real people and not professional models in the book - women that readers could relate to while learning their make-up techniques. We found six willing participants to feature as models and working with them was the most gratifying experience of writing this book. We spent many hours together perfecting the techniques in this make-up book, but their stories are also inspirational and demonstrated to us how make-up can truly make a difference. We hope you will be inspired and empowered by this book to produce the makeup look you have always wanted

Rhona & Derek

KNOW THE BASICS

1

SKIN CARE

The secret to beautiful skin is to understand your skin type and choose the correct products accordingly.

There are four basic skin types-
Normal, Dry, Oily and Combination Skin. Your skin type is determined by how much oil (sebum) your skin is able to produce. A simple test to see how much oil is in your skin is to wash your face and leave your skin product free for about half an hour. After this time place a tissue over your face and gently press it in, peel it off and any oily patches will become visible on the tissue

Skin care quiz
Take five minutes to try out a quick quiz to try and determine your skin type.

This is vital to help you to choose the correct skincare and makeup products. It is meant as a guide only.

For more information or a detailed analysis, visit your local dermatologist or skin care specialist.

1. With no makeup or moisturiser on how does your skin feel?

A Tight and flaky
B Smooth and even
C It looks shiny (especially on the forehead and nose area)

2. What is your pore size?

A Small
B Normal
C Large on Nose, Forehead and Cheeks

3. How often do you break out in spots?

A Hardly ever
B Occasionally perhaps during or after a period
C Often – I suffer regular spots/acne

4. How does your skin usually look by midday?

A Flaky patches appearing
B Fresh and clean
C Shiny, particularly in the T Zone

5. How often do you need to powder your nose to stay shine-free?

A I don't use powder - it looks patchy on my face
B Once a day is enough but not necessary
C Lots, I always get shiny patches

What skin type are you?

- **Mostly A's** - Most Likely Dry & Sensitive Skin
- **Mostly B's** - Most likely Normal Skin
- **Mostly C's** - Most likely Oily Skin

If your answers are mixed, it's most likely you have *Combination Skin* - a combination of 2 or more skin types.

See explanation and skincare tips on the following pages.

Mostly A's: You may have Dry/Sensitive Skin.

Dry skin generally feels tight and may have visible flaking especially after cleansing. It's more likely to have a matte finish, small pores, and tends to age prematurely.

Because your skin is dry it may also be prone to sensitivity. Sensitive skin is prone to redness and blotchy patches which often reacts to products (especially if perfumed) and food types with a burning, stinging, itchy tight feeling.
Sensitive skin also burns more easily in the sun.

To Care for Dry and Sensitive Skin:

- Choose products that are alcohol free, hypoallergenic and fragrance-free and where possible made of natural ingredients. They gently refresh dry skin without causing irritation, while respecting it's balance of moisture.
- Always use a creamy cleanser on the face to remove your makeup and traces of dirt. Tone using a light toner (like Rose Water) and while the skin is still damp, massage in a creamy moisturiser.
- Drink plenty of water and avoid spicy foods, caffeine and alcohol

- Always wear a good sunscreen with a good SPF.
- If showering or bathing every day make sure to moisturise extra well. This will help your skin maintain the oils that are so essential to keeping it hydrated.
- Hot water strips moisture from your skin so use warm water for baths and showers.
- Using a humidifier in your room in the winter will help keep your skin hydrated.

Mostly B's: You most likely have Normal Skin

You are the luck ones! Normal skin is healthy skin- generally very well balanced in that it's not too dry or not too oily.

It produces the correct amount of oil so that it is utilized efficiently within the skin's layers keeping it healthy and blemish-free.

Skin tone is clear and the pores are normal in size. Skin is firm, supple and tends to be free of lines and wrinkles.

To Care for Normal Skin:
- Get into a good skincare routine – cleanse, tone and moisturise twice daily.
- Exfoliate once or twice a week.
- Use a good SPF to avoid sun damage
- Drink plenty of water to keep your skin hydrated.

Mostly C's: You most likely have Oily Skin

Oily skin tends to be shiny with large open pores. The skin over produces oil (Sebum) therefore clogging pores and making you prone to blackheads, spots and blemishes.
It is very common in teenagers and can often be present during pregnancy and hormonal changes due to the imbalance of hormones.
On a lighter note people with oiler skin tend to age better as they don't get as many wrinkles!

To care for Oily Skin:
- Oily skin needs special cleansing with plenty of warm water and soap to prevent the pores from being clogged. Avoid bath or body soap which can be too severe for the face.
- Choose your cleanser with care. Avoid

heavy cleansing creams and the use of harsh soaps or cleansers.

- Try an antibacterial cleansing lotion or a lightly medicated soap, and use it in combination with a water rich in minerals, not tap water.
- Do not use cleansers or lotions that contain alcohol. After cleansing, apply a natural oil-free moisturizer to keep the skin supple.
- Wear a sunscreen with an SPF of at least 15 every day.
- Avoid skincare products that leave your skin feeling taut and dehydrated. They cause the upper layers of the skin to shrink which then restricts oil flow through the pores leading to blockages and breakouts.

Mixture of A's, B's and C's: You most likely have Combination Skin

Combination Skin refers to people who have a combination of two different skin types. Because the nose, chin and the centre of the forehead (the T- Zone) all have more oil glands than any other part of the face, it is not surprising that those areas tend to be oilier and may break out more frequently than other areas.At the same time, the areas that lack oil glands can become dry and flaky. Problems occur when you attempt to treat combination skin with the same product.

Many ingredients that are appropriate for the T-Zone won't help the drier parts of cheeks, eyes, or jaw areas and vice versa. More often than not, separate products are required to deal with the different skin types on your face.

To Care for Combination Skin:

- Avoid using harsh cleansers that are formulated for oily skin or milky cleansers made for dry skins. Instead use a good facial wash – the foaming action will help strip the oil on the oilier areas but wont dehydrate the dryer areas.
- To get rid of blackheads try using a pore strip – little sticky pads you place over blocked pores and then pull off. They are perfect for combination skin as they focus the treatment only on that area.
- Exfoliate - choose a mild exfoliating peel or scrub to de-flake the skin. Use as directed. If this causes irritation, discontinue use.
- If using both a moisturizer and acne treatment, apply the treatment, let dry, and then apply the moisturizer.

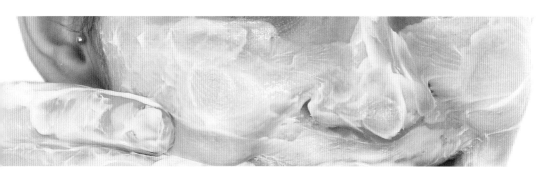

TONE, CLEANSE &
MOISTURISE

What is a Cleanser?

A Cleanser is a skincare product that is used to remove makeup dead skin cells, oil and grime from the skin and helps to unclog pores preventing skin conditions such as blackheads and unwanted spots.

Cleanser is used before toner and moisturiser as part of a daily skin care routine
Using a cleanser to remove makeup and dirt is considered to be a better alternative to soap and water because it can be specifically formulated for your skin type.

Eye Makeup Removers

This product quickly removes eye makeup without harsh wiping.
Soak a cotton pad with the remover and leave on the eyes for a minute to loosen mascara and eye makeup.
Then gently wipe away the residue. For long wear mascara and liners use a Long Wear Makeup Remover like Estee Lauder "Take it Away"

What is a Toner for?

A Toner is used to remove the residue of cleansers and makeup and helps tighten pores preventing dirt from clogging the skin. They can help very oily skin by helping to make pores appear smaller.

How do I use a Toner?

Use a spritzer and spray onto the face or apply to damp cotton pads and gently wipe the face. Be sure to use an alcohol free toner on any skin that is dry, mature, sensitive or dehydrated. A toner shouldn't sting your face but should leave your skin feeling refreshed and clean.

What is a Moisturiser?

A moisturizer is a lotion or a cream which is applied after the skin has been cleansed and toned, before putting on makeup or even if someone isn't wearing any makeup. It protects the skin from the harsh elements of the climate and work environment. It locks in skin's natural moisture and prevents the skin from drying out. It is recommended to choose a moisturiser with a SPF all year round.

Choose a moisturiser to suit your skin type:

- **Dry Skin, Sensitive and Mature Skin** – Use a moisturising cream which is oil based which will absorb quickly into the skin making it feel more soft and supple.

- **Normal Skin** – Use a lightweight

moisturiser to maintain healthy skin

- **Oily or Combination Skin** – Use an oil free lotion for oily skin. Non comedogenic moisturisers mean they are especially formulated to prevent pores clogging and will minimise their appearance.

Application of creams – Cleanse and tone the face properly. With clean hands, warm the cream between your palms to activate the ingredients. Gently massage the cream into the face working upwards until the product is completely absorbed.

Lips

Dry or chapped lips are not only unsightly but can be uncomfortable but can also invite infection. One of the most common causes is the environment - cold, wind and sun.

To treat dry or chapped lips apply some lip balm and gently exfoliate with a clean tooth brush to remove excess skin. After apply a thick layer of petroleum jelly to re-moisture them.

To prevent Lips drying out

- Apply lip balm before going outdoors to protect them from harsh weather.
- Use a balm with sufficient SPF protection all year round.
- Avoid frosted lipsticks that tend to be more drying on the lips.
- Stop smoking which can dry out the lips

HOMEMADE FACE
MASKS

Why spend a fortune on facemasks when you probably have all the ingredients in your own kitchen to make a natural, chemical free, nutrient enriched mask of your own?
To use facemasks begin by cleansing the skin thoroughly, exfoliate if necessary, apply face mask, tone & moisturise the skin. Here's some of the most popular easy to make face masks.

Face Mask for Dry/Sensitive Skin

Blend together -

- 1 egg yolk
- 1/2 cup of peeled and mashed avocado
- 1/2 cup of peeled & mashed cucumber
- 2 teaspoons of milk powder

Apply to face, leave for 10 minutes and rinse.

Face Mask for Dry Skin

- 1 egg yolk
- 2 tsp. almond oil
- 1 ripe banana

Combine everything in a bowl and mush into a paste with a fork. Apply this to face and leave on for 20 minutes. Remove with cool water and pat dry.

Face Mask for Normal Skin

- 1 egg yolk
- 1 tsp. honey
- 1 tsp. almond oil

Mix all ingredients together, stirring until smooth. To use, apply to face and rinse with warm water after 15 minutes.

Face Mask for Normal Skin Prone To Spots

Blend together-

- 1/3 cup of cocoa powder
- 1/4 cup of honey
- 2 tablespoons of heavy cream
- 3 teaspoons of oatmeal powder

Leave on the skin for 20 minutes, before rinsing away with tepid water.
Do mask once every 1-2 weeks.

Face Mask for Oily Skin 1

Blend together-

- 1 teaspoon of honey
- 2 teaspoons of ground almonds
- 1/2 teaspoon of lemon juice

Blend ingredients, apply to face and gently massage into skin.
Leave on the skin for 10 minutes and rinse.

Face Mask for Oily Skin 2

Blend together-

- 3 pineapple chunks
- 3 mango chunks
- 1 tablespoon of rolled oats
- 2 tablespoons of honey

Blend ingredients in a blender until smooth, apply and leave for 10 – 15 minutes and rinse

Homemade Toner

- **Oily Skin** – Try lemon juice as a toner - Apply freshly squeezed lemon juice with a cotton ball

- **Dry/Sensitive Skin** – Try Camomile Tea as a toner – Leave a tea bag in a cup of boiled water – steep for one hour, remove tea bag, bottle and store in fridge

- **Normal/ Dry Skin** – Try Rosewater as a toner - To gently balance and tone, apply rose water with a cotton pad (available cheaply in chemists).

Hair Mask for Dry Hair

Blend in a bowl-

- 1/4 part of avocado
- 1/4 part mayonnaise
- Comb through hair and pop on a shower cap to keep on the hair. Rinse after 15-20 minutes with a mild shampoo.

Exfoliator for Dry Hands

2 tablespoons of almond oil
1 tablespoon of sugar

TOP TIPS TO REDUCE AND PREVENT PUFFY EYES

The best way to reduce and prevent puffy eyes is of course getting enough sleep and a balanced diet and exercise but here are some quick tips for keeping eyes beautiful:

 Put two spoons in the freezer for a few minutes, place a tissue over your eyes and then rest the spoons gently against your eyelids – this will help to reduce the swelling

Save your tea bags after use, squeeze them gently and apply to the eyes for 10 – 15 minutes – a sure eye brightener for the morning after the night before

Thinly slice a small potato or cucumber and apply to the eye area. Lie down and relax for 20 minutes. This will draw out excess fluid reducing baggy eyes.

Mix together and massage well into the hands for 2 minutes, paying particular attention to dry areas.

Rinse with tepid water and pat dry. Can also be used on the feet and body and feel the amazing difference in your skin (not recommended for the face though)

Face Exfoliator (any skin type)

Scrape the inside of an avocado skin and you will be left with a grainy substance, mix this with a little olive oil and gently massage onto face.

Rinse with tepid water and pat dry. Ideal before use of a face mask

Facial Exfoliator for Sensitive and Mature Skin

Soak some cotton pads in milk for 10 minutes and apply gently to face and eyes. The acid in the milk breaks down dead skin cells and makes the skin softer and more radiant.

Rinse with warm water after.

TOP TIPS FOR SKINCARE

Glowing skin comes from within - you are what you eat! Avoid processed and junk food and eat lots of fruit and veg.

Be gentle with your skin - don't drag your skin when applying skincare or makeup products. The skin around your eyes is thinner and particularly vunerable to showing signs of aging.

Sleep well - try to get as much sleep as possible. We need at least 6 hours sleep to function properly. However the ideal amount of sleep to look wide eyed and youthful is about 8 hours per night.

Give up smoking - smoke speeds up the ageing process because it strips your skin of oxygen and slows down the rate at which new cells are regenerated. Smoking can cause fine lines around the mouth and makes the skin look grey and sluggish.

Declare your face hands off area - your fingers have more bacteria on them than you can imagine

Dry and Chapped lips are never pretty so condition them by applying a bit of lip balm and gently brush them with an old tooth brush

Massage moisturiser onto your face using circular motions rather than just slapping it on your face – it gets the circulation going and adds radiance to the skin

Drink lots of water – Like healthy food, water will help to prevent dehydration of the skin so drink at least 6 – 8 glasses a day

Opened bottles of lotions or creams will last no more than 6 months. If you detect a change of colour, consistency or smell in the product get rid of it straight away

If your skin is particularly sensitive or unpredictable ask for a sample of the product to try out before you buy it.

Going on holidays? Keep your skin glowing while flying by applying moisturiser regularly during the flight.

More isn't always better – a pea sized amount of moisturiser is enough for your face

Don't squeeze spots – some pimples are so deep that they never really come to a head – squeezing them will only make them bigger

Blotchy skin – avoid hot showers, spicy foods, caffeine and alcohol!

Eye bags can be reduced but dark circles under the eyes can't – that's what we have concealer for

Some skin problems can be easily sorted with a quick trip to a dermatologist.

MAKEUP BRUSHES

There are so many different types of brushes but what do they do and which ones do you need? Having a good set of makeup brushes is vital to creating a flawless makeup look.

You don't have to spend a fortune buying a big set of brushes – a few good quality brushes will do the job. Remember with proper care brushes can last you a long time so they are worth investing in.

There are two types of brushes: Synthetic and Natural

Synthetic Brushes work best for working with liquids or creams like foundation and concealer etc. They are generally stronger, stiffer hair to give you more control on application

Natural Bristles (such as sable, goat, pony and squirrel) are best for working with eye shadows, blushers and powder based products because they are soft and make blending very easy. They are a little more expensive but are much gentler on the skin.

TYPES OF BRUSHES

Foundation Brushes

Although a lot of women use sponges or their fingers, a foundation brush will give you the most flawless finish using a lot less makeup.

A brush will not absorb as much makeup as a sponge making it more economical to use.

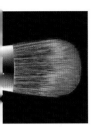

The flat foundation brush- A flat synthetic brush used for liquid, cream or cake makeup. To avoid streaks use this by gently stroking the brush back and forth to blend in the makeup. Be sure to avoid the hairline and eyebrows.

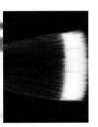

The rounded foundation brush - Carefully dip only the tips of this brush into liquid foundation and swirl the brush in circular motions from the inside of the face outwards to blend the foundation – with practice this will give you the most flawless finish.

Sponge - Lightly dampen the sponge and dab the makeup onto the face using short strokes rather than dragging the skin. It is very important to make sure the sponge is cleaned or replaced after use to avoid a build up of bacteria.

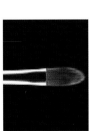

Concealer - a small flat synthetic brush used to apply concealer to small or specific areas. Some concealer brushes will be tapered at the end to help you conceal smaller areas on the face.

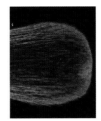

Powder Brush - Usually made of goat hair these are large fluffy brushes used to dust powder over the face after applying foundation. Keep a separate brush for bronzer so you don't end up getting tangoed by accident.

top tips

TOP TIPS FOR CHOOSING YOUR MAKEUP BRUSHES

Discard the small double ended applicators that come with eye shadows and blushers. You will not be able to get a well blended eye makeup application using them as they fall apart quite easy and are hard to clean – invest in a few good eye makeup brushes instead

Check how the brush hairs feel - against your skin – If they feel coarse or hard they are likely to irritate the skin. Makeup brushes should feel soft and comfortable on the skin.

Brushes that shed a lot of hair - are usually of poor quality. Do take care however when washing your brushes not to wet the base of the bristles too much which can cause the glue holding the hairs in place to loosen therefore causing them to fall out.

My recommendations - for the best quality makeup brushes would be MAC and Makeup Forever

Powder Puff – A round velour puff to press powder onto the face. Use a clean powder brush in a downwards direction to sweep away excess powder

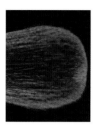

Blusher – Used to accentuate the cheeks bones. They can be rounded or angled to allow more control in application. Be sure to choose a brush with a head small enough to just cover the apples of your cheeks – otherwise you will end up with blusher all over your face.

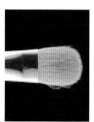

Fan Brush – Used to sweep away translucent powder or remains of eye shadow from under the eyes

Eyes

There are numerous eye shadow brushes on the market today. Just remember that the larger the eye brush the larger the area it's used on and the smaller the brush the more definition you will get. Here are the main ones that I recommend for everyday use.

Large Flat Eye shadow Brush – Use this brush to apply your base colour eye shadow by patting it on from the lashes to the brows

Medium Flat Eye shadow Brush – Used to apply eye shadow to specific areas e.g. the lids

Socket Line Brush – A small dome shaped brush used to apply or blend eye shadow into the crease of the eye

Blending Brush – A long fluffy brush tapered at the end in a dome shape used to blend away any harsh lines

Thin Eyeliner Brush – A small, very thin brush used to draw a thin line on the lashes using gel, liquid or cake eyeliner

Angled Eyeliner Brush – A soft but firm angled brush used for eyeliner or for applying eye shadow under the eyes

Angled Eyebrow Brush A brush with firm bristles used to apply colour to the brows. The angle of the brush will help to recreate short hair like movements on the brow.

Eyebrow Comb – A small applicator used to brush the eyebrows into shape on one side and to separate and unclog lashes on the other side

Lips

Although not necessary for using on yourself a good lip brush will give you a better outline of your lips

OTHER ESSENTIAL TOOLS

Pencil Sharpener – be sure to invest in a good cosmetic pencil sharpener. Eye & lip pencils are made from waxes where normal pencils are made from lead and are much stronger

Eyelash Curler – Great for giving extra curl to straight eyelashes

Tweezers – Invest in a good set of tweezers to make plucking and false eyelash application a lot easier

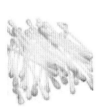

Cotton Buds – Essential for cleaning up little mistakes or blobs of mascara

Cotton Pads – used with cleansers and toners to remove makeup

MAKEUP SHELF LIFE

Did you know makeup has an expiry date? Check underneath or at the back of the product and you will see a jar like symbol with a number on it. The number represents the amount of months the product should last from the time of opening to the time it should be discarded and replaced. Here is a guide for makeup and cream products:

Foundations	24 Months
Concealer	24 Months
Powders	24 Months
Pencils	12 – 18 Months
Eye Shadow	24 Months
Mascara	6 Months
Blusher	24 Months
Lipstick	12 – 18 Months
Moisturiser	24 Months
Eye Creams	6 Months
Sunscreen	24 Months

HYGIENE AND CARE FOR YOUR BRUSHES AND TOOLS

Makeup Brushes

It is essential to clean your brushes regularly both for hygiene reasons and to keep them in good shape. With proper care good makeup brushes can last for years.

Foundation, concealer and any brushes used with liquid should be cleaned on a daily basis, powder brushes should be cleaned at the very minimum once a week depending on use.

There are a few different ways to clean your brushes:

- **Brush Cleanser –** Available with most professional brands. Simply spray it on the brushes and wipe them clean on a tissue.

- **Surgical Spirits –** Used the same as a brush cleanser but cheaper to buy and available from most chemists
- **Shampoo –** Rinse your brushes with a little warm water. Apply a small amount of a mild (or baby) shampoo and gently lather the brushes. Rinse thoroughly under running warm water until all the makeup is removed. Allow to air dry overnight.

When washing brushes make sure you are gentle with the hairs so they don't go out of shape. If they do try wrapping them tightly in a tissue when they are wet and leave them to dry. They should remould into shape when they dry out.

Other tools

- **Sponges -** should be washed after every use and replaced regularly.

- **Powder Puffs -** Wash your powder puff on a regular basis using shampoo or liquid soap and warm water. Remove all traces of makeup and leave out to dry overnight.

- **Tweezers/Eyelash Curlers -** Clean after use by spraying with surgical spirits to disinfect them.

- **Makeup Palettes and Compacts -** Clean regularly by wiping excess powder around the edges with a clean baby wipe or a cotton bud dipped in surgical spirits

TOP TIPS FOR COSMETIC SHOPPING

So now you have decided to update your makeup bag and throw out the makeup you bought six years ago that you swore you would use some day!! Its time for a new you but where do you start?

Are you intimidated by the gorgeous girls working behind the counters in department stores? Do you test your foundation in the shop and always end up with the wrong colour when you get home? Well here are some tips for going makeup shopping to make it easier for you....

- Make a list of the makeup that you need for your makeup bag – stick to that list when you go shopping so you don't end up buying half the shop and not the products you needed. When you have them in hand then you can shop till you drop to suit your budget.

- Research the internet for new products on the market and read feedback from people who have used the products before you buy them.

- When testing for foundation – remember the lighting in most of the shops is artificial therefore it will look different in natural light. Test a few foundation colours on your jaw line and go outside to natural light to see which colour disappears into your skin – that one is the correct colour for you. For more tips see the section on foundations.

- Don't be pressurised into buying a product from pushy sales staff – remember some of them are working on a commission only basis and are out for a quick sell – take your time and test the product properly first.

- Remember just because the colour eye shadow on the stunning young sales assistant looks fabulous on her – doesn't mean it will suit you.

- Keep your receipts – most stores and brands will refund or replace your product if you are not satisfied with the product (time limits may apply).

- Pick and choose the best products from different brands rather than sticking to just one. You could be limiting yourself by staying with one brand only.

- When you intend doing a big makeup shopping trip, book yourself in for a makeup lesson or makeup application first. Most brands charge a small fee for these but the amount is redeemable against products so you end up getting the lesson/application for free. In doing this you get to see the products on your skin to be sure you are buying the correct ones for you.

- Check for makeup online – you can buy professional brands of makeup for discounted prices through the internet but be sure it's from a reputable website and watch for extra shipping charges.

- Art and craft shops have a wide range of high quality brushes for half the price of professional brand makeup brushes – great for small or odd shaped brushes like eyeliner brushes etc.

- Buy supplies like makeup sponges, powder puffs, pencil sharpeners from chemists or supermarkets – they work out much cheaper than buying from professional makeup companies

- Ask for samples of foundations, creams etc and try them out at home for a day or two to be sure they are suitable for your skin rather than buying them straight away and ending up with a product you don't like.

- When comparing different prices in products take into account the quantity of product you are getting. Sometimes one brand is half the price of the other but if you're only getting half the quantity it may not be worth while.

- Check in magazines for upcoming promotions, coupons and special offers for makeup rather than finding out about the bargains after you have spent a fortune!

- Most brands will have free gifts with different promotions – its a great way to try out trial products without buying the full size product first and then you have handy containers for filling up when travelling abroad

HAPPY SHOPPING!

LEARN THE
SECRETS

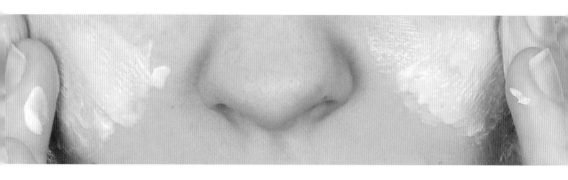

PRIMERS & CONCEALERS

PRIMERS / PREBASE PRODUCTS

Primers are the secret ingredient in every makeup artist's kit! Fairly new to the market a primer is a must have product applied after moisturiser and before foundation or on its own if you're not wearing makeup. It is normally a gel or creamy formula and is available for different skin types. Here are some of the benefits:

Functions

- It acts as a protective base giving the skin a smooth feel.
- It can reduce excess shine coming through your makeup
- It reduces enlarged pores making them less visible
- Your makeup will last a lot longer as the foundation sticks to the primer rather than your skin
- It nourishes and hydrates very dry skin
- Some primers have SPF already in them

- protecting the skin
- Improves the overall quality, texture and tone of the skin
- Disguises small flaws, red patches or imperfections on the skin
- Improves the application of foundation

Types of Primer:

- **Oil free** – great for oily skin
- **Pore Minimizing** – great for anyone who suffers with large pores
- **Hydrating** – for anyone with dryer skin
- **Colour correcting Primer** – for use under foundation for anyone with high colouring
- **Illuminating Primer** – gives dull skin a nice glow

CONCEALERS

What is a concealer?

A concealer or colour corrector is a type of makeup used to mask spots, dark circles, thread veins and other small blemishes visible on the skin. Concealer can do a good job of hiding blemishes by blending the imperfection into the surrounding skin tone or by toning down high colouring. Predominantly used by women more but more and more, men are also starting to use concealer to improve their looks. The key to a flawless complexion is with the correct use of concealer.

The choice of a concealer type also depends on the area you want to cover and all have a different purpose for example hiding enlarged pores or small spots may require a light concealer, hiding acne, dark circles, or eye bags would need to be slightly heavier but for concealing bruises, medical scars or tattoos you will need a specialised product. Some concealer can be used by itself or by mixing it with your foundation or primer.

Types of Concealer

- **Sheer** – liquid concealer
- **Pencil** – like a lip liner except these pencils are skin toned
- **Creamy** – normally in a tube with a wand or brush
- **Cakey** – paste like concealer sold in a palette or pot
- **Camouflage** – heavy concealer used to cover tattoos and bruises

Coloured Concealers

- **Colour Correcting Concealer** - yellow, green, white etc.
- **Skin Colour Concealer** - matching your skin tone.
- **Highlight Concealer** - brightening concealer for the eyes.

COMMON PROBLEMS AND HOW TO CONCEAL THEM

Dark Circles under the eyes

Under-eye circles are mostly hereditary, and tend to become more pronounced as you age but they can also be due to too much sodium, alcohol, tiredness, stress or overuse of heavy eye creams. Aging causes the skin beneath the eye to thin even more, allowing the blood vessels to show through the skin. Sometimes

top tips

TOP TIPS FOR PRIMER

- Always try to choose one with a good SPF
- Apply using a clean sponge, foundation brush or using your fingers to a cleansed or moisturised face
- For oily T Zones use a mattifying primer on the T Zone only and a hydrating primer on any dry areas.

Ones to try –
MAC Prep and Prime for Face, Smashbox Photo Finish, Estee Lauder Perfectionist, Clarins Beauty Flash Balm

a foundation alone would be enough to cover dark circles under the eyes but in some cases you will need to use a concealer.

For a subtle lift:

Apply a foundation or concealer one to two shades lighter than your foundation and gently pat under the eyes

For Darker Circles

If the dark circles are showing through your foundation you can mix a small amount of highlight concealer with your foundation and pat under the eye area to subtly lighten the foundation colour under the eyes. Try Yves Saint Laurent Touche Eclat.

For Extremely Dark Circles

Try dabbing a yellow or salmon colour correcting concealer gently onto the darker areas under the eyes and on the lids if necessary. This corrective colour will counteract the dark areas hence brightening them. This is applied before foundation after your primer. Try Benefit Lemon Aid or La Roche- Posay Yellow Concealer Pen. For darker skin tones use a peach/orange colour corrector depending on how dark the skin is. Finish by applying your foundation.

Red Thread Veins, Blotchy Skin, Spots

Areas of the skin that are redder than others need to be toned down before applying foundation – otherwise you will still see them through the makeup.

Typically a green concealer was used to conceal redness however the skin tends to look ashy after applying foundation. I recommend using a yellow concealer to tone down any redness or red spots on the face. Be sure to use a cotton bud or clean brush to apply to spots to avoid spreading infection. Apply foundation and powder over this.

If you suffer from flushed cheeks when you're out you can apply a colour correcting primer

TOP TIPS FOR CONCEALER

- Remember a Corrective Concealer brightens the skin whilst a highlight concealer with lighten the skin
- Don't forget to conceal the inner corners of the eyes as they are generally the darkest areas of the face.
- Be sure to only apply the lighter concealer to the darker areas otherwise you may give the appearance of a bag under the eyes.
- If using your fingers to apply the concealer, use your ring finger and dab it on and never stretch or pull the skin around the eyes
- For best results use a small concealer brush to apply concealer for the small areas around the eyes as it will get to the hard to reach areas and blend better for you.
- A little goes a long way – start with a small amount, blend well and add more thin layers if required
- Set concealer with a small amount of translucent powder if you find the concealer creasing

over the cheek area before applying foundation to help reduce the colour coming through the makeup later in the day

For spots and blemishes you can use a skin colour concealer the same shade as your foundation to mask any blemishes. Be careful - If you apply a highlight concealer (like Touche Eclat) over spots it will actually make them appear more prominent. Use a tapered concealer brush or cotton bud to apply the concealer but don't rub in – simply blend into the skin around the spot. Powder if necessary and then apply foundation.

Puffy Eyes

Puffy eyes are caused by fluid colleting under the skin. The swelling which results from this can form puffiness or as it's more commonly known "bags" under the eyes. Depending on the cause, the puffiness is usually temporary. If the problem is due to stress, lack of sleep, allergies or illness, then addressing the underlying cause will take care of the puffy eyes as well. Hormone changes can also lead to fluid retention, intensifying the appearance of under eye bags. More difficult to deal with is the sagging of the skin which happens as we age. The reduced production of collagen and elastin make it more difficult for the skin to bounce back into place, even when the fluid has drained out.

Correcting Puffy Eyes

One of the most common mistakes women make is to apply a highlight concealer under the eyes to conceal puffy eyes. A highlight concealer is meant to brighten up dark areas and if you put them on the puffy area it will actually make it appear worse. The trick is to apply the highlight concealer only to the dark shadow under the puffy area bringing that up to normal colour therefore reducing the appearance of the puffiness.

OTHER SKIN PROBLEMS

Dry Patches on the Skin

Avoid the use of powder in these areas which will make the dry areas worse. Use a rich moisturiser followed by a creamy foundation

Freckles

So many women try to hide their freckles instead of letting them show through the makeup. If you really want to cover them, instead of using a heavy foundation– choose a lighter consistency foundation one or two shades darker than your own skin tone (nearer the colour of the freckles)& apply – BE SURE to wear some tan/bronzer on the neck and body.

Wrinkles

No makeup will conceal wrinkles but you can definitely avoid making them worse. Moisturise the skin well, don't use an oil free foundation and don't powder areas that are prone to wrinkles. Powder tends to cling to wrinkles making them stand out more. Around the lips use a lip colour lip liner to avoid lipstick bleeding. Choose creamier products for the face.

Scars and Tattoos

In general scars and tattoos are covered with specific makeup made for these. Choosing the correct colours can be difficult so to match your skin tone exactly ask a professional for advice. Try products like La Roche Posay, Derma blend or Veil who specialise in these products.

top tips

MORE TIPS FOR CONCEALER

- If you have sensitive skin, be sure to use a product that doesn't contain any chemicals that can cause allergic reactions.
- Always use a yellow based foundation as pink based foundations will only worsen your red complexion. Also, try yellow-based blushes, such as apricot instead of a pink tone.
- It is better to correct the colour by applying colour corrector first – therefore you don't have to use a heavy foundation to cover blemishes which can make the skin look cakey.
- When powdering over concealer use a small brush to set the powder only in that area.
- Have one concealer for when you are tanned & one for when you are not, otherwise, when tanned, it would act like a highlighter bringing out spots instead of concealing them.

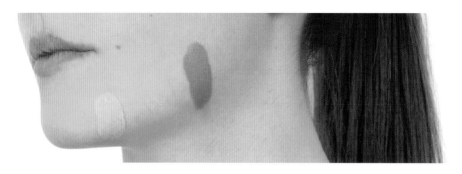

FOUNDATION & POWDER

FOUNDATION

This word alone strikes fear into most women! How do you know which type suits your skin, what colour to choose and how to apply it? A perfect makeup application begins with the correct colour foundation that blends evenly and smoothly and gives your skin a flawless, fresh look. The purpose of foundation is to even out and enhance the skin tones not to coat or hide the skin.

Choosing the shade

Your foundation should perfectly match your underlying skin tone. If you have to blend down on your neck to get rid of tide line marks your foundation is the wrong colour. The right colour should disappear into your skin when blended in.

Too often women who are pale in colour tend to choose a darker foundation to give them more colour but this will only lead to an unnatural look – instead a brush of bronzer

foundation which will minimize shine and last longer.

There are a range of different consistencies of foundation available which depend on the finished effect you want to achieve from a sheer tint to a matt full coverage finish.

- **Cream/Liquid Foundations –** A popular choice as it's easier to apply and blend and suits most skin types. They come in water and oil based formulas. If your skin is oily chose a water based (liquid) foundation which will leave a more matt finish whereas oil based (creamier) foundations are better for women with dry and mature skin who want to make there skin appear more dewy. Try Estee Lauder, La Roche-Posay, Laura Mercier, Bobbi Brown

- **Oil Free Foundations –** These foundations are great for long lasting wear and for oilier skin. Be careful not to overuse them as they can dry out the skin – always use a primer under the foundation and moisturise well if your skin is drier. Try Estee Lauder Double Wear Light or Laura Mercier Oil Free Foundation

- **Pressed Powder Compact Foundations –** These have a creamy, silky feel which appear and are applied like any pressed powder. They eliminate shine while providing good coverage so are suitable for normal to oily skin but the powder tends to flake on dry skin types. Women with very oily skin have to be careful as the foundation may appear thickened as oil reappears during the day. Try Make Up Forever Compact Powder Foundations

- **Tinted Moisturisers -** These are good for people who don't like the feel of foundation on their skin and just want to give the skin a glow. They are a lightweight, sheer consistency and are great for women looking for a natural look or used over a tan in the summer. Try Dr Hauschka Tinted Moisturisers and Foundations

will add the necessary warmth without looking unnatural. Choosing a colour that is paler than your underlying skin tone will cause the skin to look ashy. However, if your neck and body is darker than your face (due to natural or false tan) you should wear a foundation colour to match your neck and body rather than matching the foundation to the colour of the face – other wise it will be very obvious and mask like. In general most skin types are enhanced by the application of a yellow rather than a pink toned foundation colour.

To test for the correct shade, remove any makeup and apply a small line of foundation along your jaw line in natural light. Test a few colours so you can see which one of them disappears or if it's too dark or light. The colour that disappears is the correct shade for you. I would recommend having two shades of foundation – a darker one for summertime or when you may have false tan on and one for the rest of the time when you are slightly paler – in between shades can be obtained by mixing the two foundations together to get the right shade for your skin.

Types of foundation

When choosing a foundation type you have to first consider your skin type. In general dry skins need a creamier foundation with added moisturisers whilst oily skin needs an oil free

- **Mineral Makeup –** This makeup is now taking the industry by storm. So what makes mineral makeup so popular – mainly the natural ingredients? Most of the ingredients in mineral makeup are organic, pure, natural and beneficial to the skin so doesn't cause any damage if left on overnight (great for teens who forget to take off their makeup at night).
It is suitable for all skin types but note the following.

Mineral Makeups

- **Dry Skin–** in general mineral makeup suits dry and mature skin as it's not heavy and glides over the face rather than sitting into wrinkles. Use a creamy mineral foundation first and set with a light dusting of mineral powder.
- **Acne/Oily Skin –** mineral makeup is great for oily skin but be careful of the ingredients. Although it is all mineral, check for ingredients like bismuth oxchloride (which can clog the pores), alcohol (drying), talc, and dimethicone (causes blemishes). These ingredients can irritate the skin, making the acne or oily production worse. Instead look for Zinc Oxide which is a natural inflammatory and helps to heal the skin.
- **Sensitive Skin –** Mineral makeup is perfect for sensitive skin as in general it uses all natural ingredients, however be aware if you have skin that burns easily in the sun. Some products will contain the ingredient Titanium Dioxide, a natural mineral that offers sun protection. This will not be enough to offer full protection so use a moisturiser with a good SPF underneath.
- **Mineral Makeups to try:,** L'Oreal Paris, Jane Iredale, Emani Mineral Makeup

Light Reflecting Foundation

If you want your skin to look younger, use a lightweight, medium coverage foundation that moisturises the skin whilst evening out your skin tone. The foundation should contain light reflecting pigments that will give your skin a youthful glow and not sink into wrinkles. However you may need to use a corrective concealer beforehand to cover any thread veins or blemishes.

Airbrush Foundation

Used by professionals mostly, makeup is applied using an air compressor and

top tips

TOP TIPS FOR FOUNDATION

- Let foundation settle for a few minutes to see the true application.
- If your foundation when applied is too light apply a light dusting of bronzer to warm it up.
- When mixing foundation colours you need to use the same brand and type of foundation ie oil free and moisturising foundations won't mix together
- If your skin has areas with lighter pigmentations use a different colour foundation on the lighter areas to blend it all in together
- For darker skin tones - if the foundation looks ashy on your skin then you have chosen the wrong colour foundation
- Don't feel you have to apply foundation all over your face if you have good skin – you can just apply it in the areas that need coverage and use a moisturiser and prebase on the other areas instead.
- If you have combination skin you should treat the different skin types differently and use products accordingly– If the skin is oilier in the T Zone use a mattifier to combat that problem before applying a creamy foundation or use a hydrating primer under the foundation on dryer areas when using an oil free foundation

specialised makeup. The result is a natural, flawless finish used a lot for television and photo shoots but becoming more popular for wedding and special occasion makeup.

Applying foundation

The best way to apply foundation is using a foundation brush, a sponge or your fingers

- **Foundation Brush** – there are various types of foundation brushes on the market today. Using a brush will blend the makeup into the skin easier and use a lot less product
- **Sponges** – Lightly dampen the sponge before applying foundation to help it blend better. Sponges tend to drag the skin and are very unhygienic unless cleaned after every use
- **Fingers** – Using your fingers is a great way of applying foundation as the natural warmth of your hands can help the foundation to glide onto the face. Be sure to clean your hands before applying.

POWDERS

What are the functions of powder?

Powder is used to set the foundation and concealer ensuring it lasts longer and eliminates shine on the face. The powder absorbs the moisture or oil in the makeup creating a smooth matt finish on the skin.

top tips

TOP TIPS FOR POWDER

- After applying powder check the eyebrows and remove any excess powder with an eyebrow comb or a cotton bud dipped in eye makeup remover to avoid turning the eyebrows grey or clogging them
- Keep application of powder over wrinkles and lines to a minimum to avoid accentuating fine lines
- If you skin is very dry avoid the use of powder altogether, you may not need it
- If you have combination skin – apply powder to the T Zone to eliminate oil
- Make sure the powder is blended into the skin so as not to leave the skin looking cakey
- Remember this rule – no cream over powder – if you use a creamy product over powder ie cream blush or eye shadow, it will not mix and end up clogging your makeup. Use a powder over cream makeup to set it if desired
- Use the powder from the same brand as your foundation – they have been made to work with each other. Working with 2 different brands of powder and foundation may not give the best result
- If you always end up having a white face in photos even though you are darker in real life check your powder for ingredients such as titanium dioxide and iron oxides. These ingredients are light reflective and can cause a flash back on photographs.
- Always apply a little dusting of powder over neck and chest to blend in with the face

Choosing your powder

Powder should feel silky to the touch and have a very fine consistency. They come in a range of colours.

- **Translucent Powder –** this is a powder that when applied doesn't change the colour of your foundation. It does however come in several tinted colours so choose a yellow toned powder for paler skin or an orange toned powder for darker skin tones.

- **Colourless Powder –** this is a white powder so it has no pigment at all. It doesn't affect the foundation colour and is used a lot with television makeup.

- **Tinted Powder –** if choosing a tinted

powder be sure that it perfectly matches your foundation colour to avoid changing the colour of the face.

- **Iridescent Powder –** this is a shimmery powder which can be used on the body or as a highlighter on the face – don't apply all over the face as it can accentuate lines, wrinkles, scars and blemishes.

Types of powder

- **Pressed Powder –** comes in a compact form, great for a light application and for touch ups during the day.

- **Loose Powder –** suitable for use at home and can give a heavier application. Best for use with a powder puff and can give longer lasting results.

Application of powder

- **Large Powder Brush –** *(see left)* Using a clean, large, fluffy and rounded makeup brush dip it into the powder and tap off any excess. Apply powder in downwards strokes on the face to avoid clogging hair on the face. This method will give you the lightest application so as not to cake the makeup. Dust a small amount over the eyelids to set the concealer and foundation also.

- **Powder Puff –** using a clean velour powder puff, gently press the powder into the face in a rocking motion. Afterwards use a clean powder brush to brush down the face to remove any excess powder.

BRONZERS

Different finishes of bronzers

- **Matt Bronzers –** used for a subtle effect or for contouring the face (apply with a brush).

- **Shimmering Bronzers –** used for adding

TOP TIPS FOR BRONZER

- Take care when choosing your bronzer to choose a shade only one or two tones darker than your foundation otherwise you may end up looking tangoed
- Dust a small amount of bronzer on the shoulders and neckline to enhance a tan or warm up the skin
- Use as a blusher for darker skin tones and if you have high colouring

- Use a matt bronzer if the foundation you applied is too light, this will help to darken it subtly
- Powder bronzers work better with oily skin and gel/cream bronzers on dry skin
- Always start with a small amount of bronzer and then add more if you need it.
- If you apply too much bronzer, blend away as much of it as possible and then dust a little translucent powder over it to tone it down
- Make sure bronzer is blended well so you are not left with streaks

a sun kissed glow to the skin (apply with a brush).

- **Gel Bronzer –** used for a more sheer effect to give a glow to the skin (apply and blend with fingertips or a clean sponge)

To get the ultimate sun kissed look apply bronzing powder or cream to areas that are normally hit by the sun ie the cheekbones, the bridge of the nose, the temples and the chin rather than applying it all over the face.

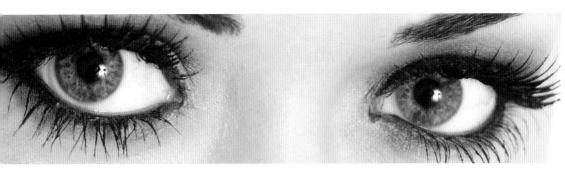

EYE MAKEUP

Your eyes are the first thing people see when they look at your face. With all applications of makeup be it natural or dramatic, care should be taken to make sure the eyes are made a feature. The purpose of eye makeup is to make the eyes stand out not necessarily the eye makeup. With the correct application and blending there can be an amazing difference to both your eye shape and eye colour.

TYPES OF EYE MAKEUP

- **Eye shadow**
- **Eye liner**
- **Mascara and False Lashes**

EYE SHADOW

Eye shadow comes in two main forms – powder and cream.

- **Powder Based Shadows –** come in loose or compact form. They are better for longer lasting stay and easier to blend.

- **Cream Eye Shadow –** available in stick, liquid or compact form - great for a natural look but tends to crease and doesn't last long

Eye Shadows can also be Matt, Frosty, Shimmery, Glittery, Metallic and Glossy.

Choosing eye shadow colour

In general, eye shadow colours should not match the colour of your eyes. If you contrast the colours it can make your eyes stand out more.

- **Blue Eyes -** Try gold, coppers, orange browns, olive greens, taupe, greys and browns. Avoid aqua colours or similar colour blues as your eyes which will only try to compete with your eye colour
- **Brown Eyes -** You can get away with most colours but try greens, violets, gold, purples, plums, peaches and greys
- **Green Eyes -** Try pinks, violets, purples and all shades of brown. Avoid silvers and blues

Use your skin tone as a guide for choosing the intensity of the colour. The lighter the skin tone, the less intense and the darker the skin tone the more intense.

Correcting Eye Shapes

Using a light, medium and darker shade of eye shadow you can subtly change the appearance of your eye shape. Here is a quick guide to help you:

- **Small Eyes -** Use a light colour on the eyelid and a darker colour in the crease of the eyelid. Highlight under the brow
- **Large Eyes -** Wear darker colours on the eyelid up to the crease and use a matt highlighter under the brow
- **Close Set Eyes -** Use a lighter colour on the inside of the eyes and a medium colour on the outer corner
- **Wide Set Eyes -** Use a lighter colour on

the eyelid and under the brow. Apply a medium colour to the socket line darkening it slightly in the inner corners of the eyes
- **Deep Set Eyes -** Apply a light colour over the entire eye area. Apply a medium tone slightly above the socket line and blend. Give more emphasis to the outer corner of the eyes by applying a darker colour to the outer corner of the lower lash line and don't highlight the brow bone
- **Hooded Eyes -** To make the eyes appear less heavy use a light colour on the lid. Then apply a medium colour starting at the outer corner of the eyes and shape upwards across the centre. Apply a darker colour over the hooded area and blend it up towards the brow bone. Be sure to blend well
- **Oriental Eyes -** Apply a light shadow over the entire eye. Recreate a socket line by blending shadow in a half moon shape on the eyes. Apply a little darker shadow to the outer corner of the lower lashes and blend well

REMEMBER:
Dark shadows can make your eyes look smaller while lighter colours can make your eyes look bigger.

Applying eye shadow
What you need:
Eye Makeup Brushes, Concealer, Foundation, Powder and 3 Eye Shadow Colours.
Most eye shadow palettes you buy will give you three complimentary shades of the same colour.

- **Base Colour -** This is the first colour you will apply with all eye shadow techniques. It can be cream (for a more natural look), white (for a more glamorous look) or shimmery white (for a dramatic look) or the palest colour of the palette
- **Medium Colour -** This would be the main colour you choose

- **Darker Colour -** This would be a darker shade of the colour you have chosen or could be a dark brown or black

Natural Look

1. Apply concealer/foundation over the eyelids and set with a light dusting of translucent powder
2. Using a large flat eye shadow brush apply a base colour all over the lids from the lashes to the brow. This will act as a subtle highlighter on the brow bone
3. Using a medium flat eye shadow brush apply a medium colour from the lashes to the socket line
4. Use your blending brush to blend away the line of makeup on the socket line so it fades upwards into the base colour

Evening Look

1. Apply concealer/foundation over the eyelids and set with a light dusting of translucent powder
2. Using a large flat eye shadow brush apply

a base colour (cream or white) all over the lids from the lashes to the brow

3. Using a medium flat eye shadow brush apply a medium colour from the lashes to the socket line
4. Use your blending brush to blend away the line of makeup on the socket
5. Looking into a mirror with your eyes open, use a socket line brush to apply a darker colour in a line from the middle of the eye out towards the outer corner. Be sure to keep to the socket line shape rather than drawing straight across.
6. Blend very well with your blending brush to get rid of any harsh lines
7. Use a shimmery white eye shadow and apply just under the eyebrows to highlight the brow bone
8. Apply a small amount of eye shadow with your angled eyeliner brush to the bottom lash line and blend away excess with a cotton bud (as desired)

This method can be used with any set of colours – just use the main colour on the lids and then blend a darker shade into the socket line.

If you want to go more dramatic add black eye shadow to the outer corners of the socket line to deepen the dark colour you used and blend

TOP TIPS FOR EYE SHADOW

- Avoid shimmery eye shadow on lined or creased eyelids as it will only highlight those areas making them look worse
- To stop eye shadow flaking under the eyes, apply some loose translucent powder under the eyes and when finished simply brush away using your fan brush
- Always use the flat part of the eye shadow brush to press the eye shadow onto the eyes rather than dragging or flicking it on. This will help you get a better application and a more intense colour.
- Be sure to apply eye shadow into the roots of the lash line so you are not left with a gap between the lashes and the eye shadow starting when you open your eyes.

well. Use a little shimmer over the lid and re highlight the brow bone to finish the look.

EYE LINER

The use of eyeliner goes back to Egyptian times (think Cleopatra). The type of eyeliner your use depends very much on the type of look you are after.

Types of eyeliner

- **Liquid Eyeliner –** This generally comes with a brush in a tube but can be tricky to apply. Allow the liquid to dry before opening your eyes to avoid it marking your eyelids. Not suitable for the inner rims of

the eyes
- **Gel Eyeliner –** A gel type formula that goes on smoothly and dries quickly. It is quite long lasting and doesn't smudge when you open your eyes making it easier to use. For best results use with an angled or thin eyeliner brush. Not suitable for the inner rims of the eyes
- **Pencil –** Creates a softer line and can be

blended with a cotton bud for a smoky look. It can be applied to the inner and/or outer rims of the eyes. Be sure to sharpen the pencil every time before use and for a longer lasting result set the pencil with a little eye shadow
- **Shadow Liners –** Use eye shadow wet or dry as an eye liner. Apply with an angled or a flat headed eye lining brush
- **White Eye Pencil –** Used to brighten up the whites of the eyes. Apply to the inner rims of the eyes for the best effect.

TOP TIPS FOR EYELINER

- Rest your elbow and use a hand mirror when applying eye liner. Move the mirror to the best position and tilt your head so you can see where you are working and get the best position possible.
- To get a thin line apply eyeliner along the roots of the lashes rather than trying to draw a line on the skin.
- To thicken the line apply as for a thin line and then carefully but slowly build this line up from the lashes until you get the desired effect.
- If you want a more dramatic look apply eyeliner after eye shadow. For a more subtle look apply eyeliner before eye shadow.
- Lining the inner rims can make the eyes look smaller but can make the colour of the eyes more piercing depending on the effect desired.
- To give your eyes more of a lift apply liner thinly on the inside corner of the lids and thicken slightly towards the outer corners.
- To make small eyes look wider bring the eye liner out a little further than where the lashes end to extend the appearance of the lash line.
- If you make a mistake with eyeliner use a cotton bud straight away to remove the product before it sets and dries.
- To avoid a gap between the lashes and the liner apply the liner as near to the lashes as possible – if you still see gaps, apply a little eye shadow in the same colour over the liner to fill the space.
- If your lashes are quite sparse and you don't want the heavy look of a liner on top of the lid, try applying some pencil to the inner rim of the upper eye – this will give the appearance of a more defined lash line. Take care as this will require practice.
- Be sure that both eyes match by looking at a mirror from a short distance rather than too close up.
- Always sharpen an eye pencil before using it to avoid contamination and infection and never share your pencil with anyone
- Good eyeliner application takes time and patience so practice makes perfect.

LUCIOUS LASHES

Everybody wants to make the best of their eyes and having longer, thicker eyelashes will help dramatically. Eyelashes have a practical function too - they protect our eyes from dust and debris.

Full eyelashes can really enhance your eye makeup making your eyes look vibrant and bigger.

Not everyone is born with thick eyelashes, but thanks to mascara and a few simple tips, anyone can achieve fuller eyelashes.

Guide to lucious lashes

Items required:
- Lash primer
- Eyelash curler
- Mascara
- Hand mirror

- Begin by using a lash primer. A primer coats the lashes and separates them before you apply mascara. Some primers come with the mascara (the white tube)
- For extra curl use an Eyelash Curler. Curling lashes gives eyes the appearance of being wider and brighter. Gently heat the

curler with warm air from your hairdryer for 3-5 seconds before curling lashes. Touch it first to make sure it's not too hot. This will give you even more curl.

- It's a myth that you have to curl lashes

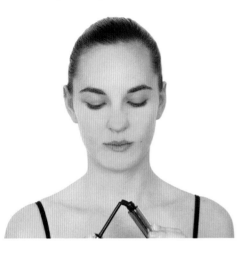

before you apply mascara. You can curl lashes after mascara application; just make sure the mascara is dry first.

- Choose the right Mascara. If you want to add body to your lashes then use thickening mascara, if you want longer lashes then use lengthening mascaras. Even if you have natural long lashes, adding lengthening mascara can give a beautiful curling effect to your eyelashes. Most mascaras now come in waterproof formula which helps them last longer and stay smudge proof

- To avoid staining your skin with mascara when applying it, follow these simple steps. For the bottom lashes - take a small hand mirror hold it above your head and look up into it but keep your chin down. For the top lashes – take the small hand mirror and hold it under your chin looking down into it. This moves your lashes away from the skin so you avoid staining the skin.

- Remove the wand from the mascara tube and as the brush comes out bend it to a 90 degree angle – this will help you to be

able to get right to the root of the lashes rather than just applying to the tips of the lashes

- Be sure to coat all your lashes – even the small lashes right at the inner corner and the outer corner otherwise you will make your lashes look narrower than they are

- Avoid clumping and smudging by blotting any excess mascara from the wand with a tissue. Wiggle the wand left to right from the base of the lashes to the tips

- Always keep your mascara wand clean and don't share your mascara with anybody, even family!

- Apply a second coat before the first coat

dries otherwise it will clump

- Don't be tempted to pump your mascara as this only introduces air into the tube which will dry out your mascara

- Be sure to replace the wand in the tube the second you are finished using it

- Mascara once opened should be disposed of and replaced every 6 months.

- If your mascara is drying up – close the lid tight and put it into a cup of boiling water for a few minutes – this will loosen it up.

False eyelashes

For extra glamour or to help fill in missing lashes you can apply some false lashes. There are two main types:

- **Full Strip Lashes –** these add density to the whole lash line but can look quite false

- **Individual Lashes –** These are small bunches of 3 to 4 lashes glued together and are best used if you want to thicken your own lashes or fill in missing lashes. They require a steady hand but make a huge but subtle difference when applied.

top tips

TOP TIPS FOR APPLYING FALSE EYELASHES

- The first step and maybe the most important one when applying false eyelashes is to start with clean eyelids. The adhesive will not adhere to oil so be sure to use an oil-free eye makeup remover and avoid any oil-based makeup near your eyes.
- Use a suitable length lash – the same length as your own if you just want to thicken them or slightly longer for a more dramatic look.
- Before applying the lashes, line your upper lash line with liner or pencil which will help conceal where the lashes are placed and will help strengthen the lash line.
- Place a small amount of glue on a spatula and lightly coat the band of the strip lashes with the glue or with individuals dip the end of the lash bunch into the glue. Leave it until it becomes slightly tacky.
- Important -Don't apply eyelash glue

directly to the skin – always to the false lashes and attach them to the eyes
- Apply the false lashes as close to your natural lash line as possible with either your fingers, a cotton bud or a tweezers (take care around the eye area).
- With individual lashes, apply them to the outside corners of the eye first and work your way inwards gluing them to the eyelashes rather than the skin – you should only need about 3 or 4 per eye.
- After you've applied the false lashes, curl them along with your real lashes and apply mascara if you wish
- To remove false eyelashes use the glue remover (most brands supply it with the lashes) instead of pulling them as eyes can be quite sensitive. If there was no remover provided use a little oil or oily based makeup remover on a cotton pad and gently press on the eyes for a few minutes. This will help to loosen the glue making them easier to remove
- To reuse your strip lashes clean them according to the instructions and remove any excess glue
- Remember Practice makes Perfect!!!

EYEBROWS

Eyebrows believe it or not are one of the most important features of your face and can change your whole expression.

Getting the eyebrows right is one of the hardest challenges for women. It is a good investment to visit a brow expert the first time you decide to shape them so they can give you advice on what suits you and then you can just pluck the hair as it grows back.

If you are going to have a go yourself then here is a guide to getting the best result.

1. For very long eyebrows begin by using an eyebrow brush to comb your eyebrows up and then carefully trim any excess that goes beyond the natural hair line. Then comb them downwards and do the same. This will remove any excess length in stray

eyebrows.

2. Take a brush or a pencil and place it vertically against your nose. It should run from the side of the nose, mid-mouth, and by the tear duct of the eye. This is your guide to where your eyebrow shape should

begin. Any hair that you see to the inside of this line should be removed

3. Looking straight ahead place the brush/pencil vertically so that it is aligned with the outer edge of the iris of the eye. This is wear your arch should be.

4. To determine where your eyebrow should end, place the pencil diagonally across to

the opposite corners of the mouth, nostril, and outside corner of the eye. Any hair that goes beyond this line should be tweezed.

5. Line the pencil/brush from the start of the eyebrow to the end of the eyebrow. The pencil should create a perfect straight line.

6. Dot your start, finish and arch position with an eye pencil and simply join the dots in a gentle arch to be the guide for your new eyebrow shape

Eyebrow makeuo

After perfecting your eyebrow shape we now need to look at the colour. By using the proper eyebrow colour and products we can all have the perfect eyebrows. Here is a look at some of the products available.

- **Eyebrow Pencil:** Most commonly used is the eyebrow pencil but is probably the most misused too. To avoid giving yourself

TOP TIPS FOR PLUCKING EYEBROWS

- Full, well-shaped brows are the final frame to the eyes. Even without eye makeup, well-groomed brows are a must. The key, of course, is to make them look as natural as possible
- Which hairs you pluck and don't pluck is the difference between attractive brows and uneven brows
- Try using a white eye pencil to draw over hairs that you are considering plucking and use a eye pencil matching your hair colour and try out different shapes to see which one suits you best
- Go slowly and don't over tweeze – you can't stick them back on!
- The best looking brows are the ones that look natural. Pencil thin or overly bushy brows can be dated looks that can be distracting rather than enhancing
- Hold the tweezers at a 45 degree angle when plucking and remember always pluck hair in the direction of the growth.
- Some hair won't grow back if it is constantly over plucked leaving you with gaps in your eyebrows.
- For less pain when tweezing your brows do it after a shower or bath where your pores are open making it easier for the hairs to come out
- To avoid infection make sure you sterilise your hands and tweezers every time before using them
- As an alternative to plucking you can also get them waxed or threaded (an Indian art of removing hair using thread and a lot of skill). For this I would highly recommend going to a professional salon to have it done.

massive thick eyebrows sharpen your pencil to a fine point and use very soft, short strokes replicating the eyebrow hair. Then blend with a firm eyebrow brush. If you apply too much colour, soften the effect with a cotton bud that has been dipped in makeup remover. Do not apply eyebrow pencil too close to the inner brow (near the nose) as this tends to create an angry-looking brow.

- **Eyebrow Powder:** Brow powder is a very matte powder with high colour pigments and provides the most natural look. Eye shadows will also do the same but ensure you use a matt colour. Begin application in the centre of the brow and work outward toward the brow tip then back toward the beginning of the brow Apply with an angle eye brush and use light strokes.

- **Mixing Powder and Pencil:** If you find eyebrow pencil doesn't last or looks smudged on then try applying a little eyebrow powder over the pencil to set it.

- **Eyebrow Gel:** Brow gel comes in clear or colour formulas.
  It is great to use if you have unruly eyebrows. If you use the clear formula, fill in first prior with an eyebrow pencil or powder and apply the gel on top.

- **Eyebrow Mascaras:** Also available in clear and colour formulas these are great for keeping eyebrows in shape as well as adding colour and definition.
  You can also spray some hair spray on your brow brush to hold them in place.

Choosing the right eyebrow colour

As a guide you can generally match the eyebrow colour to your hair colour however that doesn't work for everyone. Eyebrows tend to take colour quicker and stronger than other hair so I would recommend going a little bit lighter than your natural colour. Here is a quick colour guide:

Hair colour	Use
Blonde	Blonde/Mushroom colour powder
Dark Blonde/Light Brown	Blonde pencil or light brown powder
Brown/Dark Brown	Chestnut or medium brown pencil
Black	Soft Black or Dark Brown
Silver/Gray	Blonde
Natural Redheads	Blonde/light brown
Chosen Redheads	Auburn

CHEEKS & LIPS

CHEEKS

Blusher comes in both cream and powder and is used to add colour to the face. It should compliment the rest of your makeup particularly the lip colour. Where you put blusher is very important and it should be built up slowly to give you a natural glow rather than a stripe of colour.

Choosing a colour

Choosing a colour for blusher is where most women go wrong! A simple rule would be the fairer the skin, the lighter the shade, the darker the skin the deeper the shade. A simple test is to pinch your cheeks or look at the tone or colour you naturally go when flushed after exercise and use that colour as a guide. In general pink or peach colours look good on paler skin and darker tones work better on darker skins.

Types of Blusher

- **Powder Blusher –** this is the most

popular type of blusher - similar in consistency to pressed face powder. This works well on all skin types especially oily skin.

- **Cream Blusher –** this type of blusher is better for drier skin types. It blends on nicely giving the skin a dewy, natural glow
- **Combination Powder/Cream Blush –** A longer lasting blusher that goes on like a cream but dries to a powder finish. Suitable for most skin types
- **Blusher Tints/Gels –** a water based formula applied to the cheeks for a transparent, natural glow. These can be used over moisturiser or foundation but dry quite quickly so blending is more difficult. They are more suited for clear skin that just require a hint of colour
- **Mineral Blushers –** these blushers are highly refined and give a lovely finish to the skin. They work well on all skin types

Blusher application techniques

- **Powder Blushers -** should be applied after face powder using a soft blusher brush. Tap off excess powder from your brush, look in the mirror and smile – apply the blusher to the apples of the cheeks (the rounded area that comes up when you smile) and blend in a circular motion. Use the brush to gently sweep any excess powder upwards and outwards.
- **Cream Blushers -** is applied after foundation and set with translucent powder if required. Use clean fingers or a sponge to apply this cream to the apples of the cheeks and blend in well.

Contouring and hightlighting

The questions most people ask are what is contouring and highlighting, what products should I use and how do I do it?

What is contouring and highlighting?

- **Contouring** is a technique using a shader to create the illusion of shadow on the face

TOP TIPS FOR APPLYING BLUSHER

- As a rule if you draw an imaginary line from the bottom of your nose across to your ear- your blusher should never go below that, then looking straight ahead into a mirror, draw another imaginary line from the inner side of your eyeball straight down towards your jaw line – your blusher should never come inside that line and your nose.
- Always start with a small amount of blusher and build up the colour. It is easier to add more than to remove the excess. If that does happen however, add some translucent powder over the blusher to help tone down the colour
- Be careful of ending up like someone stuck in the 80s – the trend then was to apply blusher high on the cheekbone sweeping upwards to the temple area. Fashion trends change but you are always safe with a natural glow to the apples of the cheeks
- If you are using a dewy foundation be sure to set the cheek area with a small amount of powder before applying powder blusher – otherwise it won't blend well
- Change your colour blusher with your foundation – so if you are wearing tan or darker makeup you need to darken your blusher to suit
- After applying blusher, use your foundation brush to blend over the area – this will put a small film of foundation over the blusher, giving the illusion of colour coming through from your skin rather than blusher sitting on your face. This will give a more natural finish

therefore resculpting the shape of the face and its features.

- **Highlighting** is a technique used to bring out features in the face by using a lighter colour. It is based on the principle that light brings features out and shader makes features recede.

What products should I use?

Shaders and Highlighters are available as creams or powders. Use a matt formula for shading and a matt or iridescent formula for highlighting (depending on the strength of a highlight you want)

Shading – You can shade or contour the face using a matt bronzing powder, a foundation or a coloured pressed powder. You need to use a colour, one to two shades darker than your foundation or skin tone to have the desired effect. Be careful in your choice as contouring should look completely natural and blending is essential.

Highlighting – Use a colour two to three shades lighter than your foundation to bring out features on the face. The more dramatic the effect desired the lighter and more iridescent the highlighter should be. Try Benefit High Beam, Mac Cream Base "Luna" or even a white

shimmery eye shadow will do the trick

Where should you use it?

Shader can be used :

- On the hollow of the cheeks just under the cheekbone (to make the cheekbones look more prominent)
- Under the chin (to disguise a double chin)
- On the socket line of the eye (to give more definition to the eye socket)
- On the sides of the nose (to thin down a wide nose)
- On the temples (to add dimension to the face)
- To the hairline (to diminish a high forehead)
- To the line of your cleavage (to make the cleavage look deeper!)

Highlighters can be used:

- On top of the cheekbone (to make cheek bones look higher)
- On the centre of the eyelid (to make eyes look bigger)
- On the brow bone (to accentuate the brow)
- On the centre of the nose (to accentuate the centre of the nose after shading)
- To the collarbones (to make them more prominent)
- To the top of the breasts (to make them appear bigger!)

How do I do it?

Shading – in general for normal wear keep contouring to a minimum as it can look very unnatural if applied incorrectly.

Highlighting – Use a highlighter to accentuate cheek bones but don't apply it all over the face as it just makes the face look shiny and unnatural.

The most common area to contour and highlight would be the cheeks.

1. Start by applying foundation and powder.
2. Suck in your cheeks to find where the natural hollow is and use that as a guide

for your shading. Relax your cheeks

3. Using an angled shader or blusher brush, apply a small amount of shader to this area following the natural curve of the cheekbone.

4. Blend well with a clean brush to diminish any harsh lines

5. Now apply a little highlighter to the area above the cheekbones starting at the outer corner of the eye working up towards the temples. If using a powder highlighter you can use a small clean eye shadow blending brush or if using a cream, dot some highlighter along this line and blend in with your fingers

TOP TIPS FOR CHEEKS

- Be careful to blend all of your shading and highlighting well with a clean brush in order to diminish any harsh and obvious lines
- When using a highlighter be careful as the incorrect use can give the appearance of bags if applied too close under the eye
- Keep contouring and highlighting to special occasions or nights out
- Remember practice, practice and then practice some more!

LIPS

The application of a good lipstick or lip gloss should enhance and compliment the rest of your makeup.

Choosing the right colour and texture can be a matter of personal preference but be sure that t co ordinates with the eyes and cheeks. In this chapter I will give you some tips in choosing and applying your lipstick/lip gloss.

Types of lip products

Matt Lipsticks – are long lasting lipsticks but can be very drying on the lips. They contain less moisture than other lipsticks giving them a matter finish

Cream Lipsticks – these contain more oil and are a creamy texture. They are great for dry, mature or cracked lips

Sheer Lipsticks – these are a nearly clear lipstick with a tint of colour – great for a natural look if required.

Glossy Lipsticks – these lipsticks can look very natural or dramatic depending on the colour. They leave the lips with a glossy finish

Frosted Lipsticks – these can give a dramatic effect to the lips but not suitable for dry or mature lips

Long Lasting Lip Products – these normally come in two parts ...a lip stain and a clear gloss to go over it. Care must be taken in applying these as if you go wrong they are quite difficult to remove unless you take it off straight away. The gloss is applied when the lip stain has dried in to give some shine back to the lips. They are very drying on the lips and tend to fade out in patches over the day.

Lip Pencils – these will both define and colour the lips and can be longer lasting than lipsticks.

Use a clear gloss over it to give a more voluptuous finish.

Lip Gloss – these come in many different applicators like tubes, pots and wands. Coloured glosses are very popular for women who don't like the heavy feel or inconvenience of a lipstick. Clear glosses are great for using over a lipstick to give a dewy finish to the lips

Lip Liners – these are used to outline the lip and prevent the lipstick from bleeding.

Lip Corrector Pencils – these are skin coloured pencils used to outline just outside the lip line to correct the lip shape before applying lip pencil – see Hannah's Story for use of this pencil

Lip Sealers – these are used after the application of lipstick to seal the lip colour but can be quite drying.

Choosing Your Lipstick/Gloss Colour

Your lipstick or lip gloss should compliment your natural lip colouring and skin tone.

Remove all your makeup and look at the tone of your lips ie are they more pinky, brown, red etc. Now match a neutral lipstick with the same tone. The correct colour should make your eyes look brighter, brighten your skin tone and look natural on. When choosing a stronger lip colour, choose one of the same tone but in a darker shade.

Use this as a quick guide to choosing your colour:

- Light skin tones can use light brown beiges with pink or orange undertones
- Dark skinned tones can use warm plums, wines and deep reds
- Olive skin tones can use brownish reds, light browns and raisin shades
- Red heads suit warmer browns and should be avoid blue based lip colours such as mauves and certain reds
- Avoid pale pink lipstick or orange tones if your teeth are discoloured as these colours will make them look more yellow

Correcting your lip shape

The most natural lip shape is a fuller bottom lip and a slightly thinner top lip. As most of us have variations of this shape here are some tips:

- **For big lips** - use muted matt colours such as browns and purples and avoid using gloss and shiny lip colour. Apply foundation and powder over the lips to hide the natural lip line and then apply lip liner slightly under the natural lip shape to make them appear smaller.
- **To correct uneven lips** - such as cleft palette, scaring etc apply some foundation and powder over the lips to block out the

shape. Apply a corrective lip pencil (skin toned) outside the lip line to create a new lip shape. Just under that apply a neutral coloured lip liner and fill with lipstick. Use a cotton bud to blend away the remainder of the corrective pencil and you're left with your newly shaped lips. See page 84.

- **For thin lips -** avoid dark colours and opt for a lighter shade to make them look fuller. Define the lips by applying lip liner slightly above the natural lip line and blend downwards into the lips so you don't see the gap. Apply lipstick to your bigger lips.
- **For lips where one is larger than the other-** try using a lighter shade of the lipstick on the smaller-sized lip to make it look bigger and apply a small amount of gloss to the centre of that lip to highlight it
- **For heavy lined lips -** apply your lipstick vertically to avoid the lipstick seeping from the lips.

top tips

TOP TIPS FOR LIPS

- Be sure to sharpen your lip pencil every time before you use it. As well as sterilising the pencil, it gives you a finer point for application
- If you want to wear a dark lipstick be sure to keep your eye makeup light
- Alternatively, if you are wearing strong eye makeup choose a more neutral colour
- Never use a dark lip liner with a pale lipstick. This didn't look good in the 80's and it sure isn't in fashion now.
- When shopping for lipsticks never use a tester directly onto your lips – it is very unhygienic. Ask for a disposable lip brush or bring your own!
- Don't judge a lip colour by the label on the lipstick – try it out first before buying
- There is nothing wrong with applying your own lipstick from a tube but a lip brush will give you a more defined finish as well as using a lot less lipstick
- The older or drier your lips the more creamier a texture you should choose. Avoid matt lipsticks and glosses
- To keep lipstick from staining your glass, discreetly lick your lips before each sip.
- Lipstick on your teeth? After applying lipstick put your index finger in your mouth, close your lips around it and then pull your finger out. The excess goes on your finger rather than on your teeth
- Choose lighter colours for daytime and darker colours in the evening.
- Have you got lots of lipsticks you have never worn? Rather than throwing them out, check if any of them are a suitable colour to use as a cream blush or try mixing some of them in a pallette to create a new colour.
- To mend a lipstick that broke in half, using a tissue to hold the broken piece melt the end of it carefully with the heat from a match or lighter – when its soft place it back onto the base gently pushing it back on. Leave it in the fridge for about 20 minutes to set
- Down to the end of your favourite lipstick? Get a spatula and scrape out the end of the tube and put on a palette. Mix some Vaseline and apply to the lips with a lip brush
- Going on holidays and want to bring all your lipsticks with you? Using a sharp knife slice about 2mm off the top of your lipsticks and put each colour into a different day of a tablet dispensing/pill box and use as required.
- Does your lipstick melt in hot weather? – it is perfectly safe to store lipsticks in the fridge so they don't soften and also are cooling on the lips when applied
- Always use a lip liner to match your lipstick or for a more neutral effect use a lip liner matched to your lip colour

Lipstick Application

To apply lipstick, use the following handy steps:

1. Make sure the lips are well moisturised
2. Apply foundation and a light dusting of powder to the lips to act as a base for the lipstick
3. Apply lip liner defining or correcting the lip shape as desired
4. Relax your mouth so it opens slightly and then using a lip brush apply lipstick to the inner, fuller part of the lips first
5. With your lip brush carefully work on defining the edges of the lips blending up to the lip liner
6. Apply a small amount of gloss as desired.
7. If your lips don't need correcting apply

lip liner after the application of lipstick to prevent the lipstick from bleeding. This will give the lips a more definite shape but in a more subtle way.

Making your lipstick last longer

1. After applying your lipstick, separate a two ply tissue and use one sheet to blot the lips. Apply a light dusting of translucent powder. Reapply the lipstick and blot again using the other half of the sheet. Apply again if needed and use gloss sparingly
2. Outline and then fill in the entire lips with a lip pencil the same colour as your lipstick. Apply lip colour. When the lipstick fades the lip pencil will still be there
3. Lip Sealer can be applied after lipstick but it does tend to dry out the lips

PUTTING IT ALTOGETHER: SMOKEY EYES

To easiest way to create smokey eyes is to start by doing the eyes first. This way you can make as much mess under the eyes with falling eye shadow without ruining your base. When you have finished the eyes, simply wipe away any excess product under the eyes with a makeup remover or a wipe. Then apply foundation to the rest of the face as normal taking care to blend gently around the eyes. Smokey eyes can be done in any colour but darker colours tend to be more dramatic – try dark browns, greys, black etc

10 steps to smokey eyes

1. Apply concealer/foundation over the eyelids and set with a light dusting of translucent powder

2. Using a large flat eye shadow brush apply a base colour (cream or white) all over the lids from the lashes to the brow
3. Apply a medium to dark colour all over the lids from the lashes to the socket line.
4. Use your blending brush to blend the socket line so the colour fades into the base colour that is on the brow bone
5. For a stronger look layer some darker eye shadow to the lids of the eyes nearer the lash line. Darker eye shadow requires a few coats to strengthen the colour so reapply until you get the desired effect
6. Apply eye pencil to the inner rim of the upper/lower eyelids as preferred
7. Apply pencil/gel or liquid liner to the top of the upper lid of the eyes.
8. For a more dramatic effect apply some black or dark eye shadow under the lower lid near the lashes and blend with a cotton bud
9. Try using a little highlighter on the inner corner of the eyes if you feel your eyes look too dark
10. Apply plenty of mascara and false eyelashes for a more dramatic effect.

BEAUTY ADVICE
DURING AND AFTER
CANCER TREATMENT

skin and nail care
reccommended products
eyebrow and eyelashes care
hair and wig care

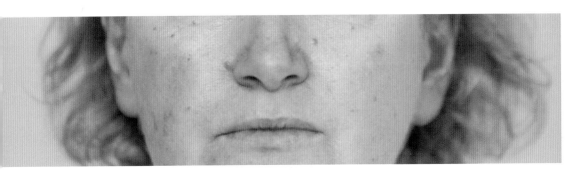

SKIN & NAIL CARE

Cancer and Cancer Treatments may cause changes to your physical appearance. Some are temporary and some permanent, which may impact your self esteem. There are many options available to each and every survivor.

Most skin reactions will resolve a few weeks after treatment has stopped. Some of the most common side effects experienced are Hair Loss, Hyper pigmentation, Hand-Foot Syndrome, Swollen Red Itchy Skin, Peripheral Neuropathy, Nail inflammation and Hypersensitivity. Some Chemotherapeutic agents cause skin rashes characterized by inflammatory papules and irritation of the face, neck and upper trunk. Some patients may experience irritation, cracking and peeling of the skin on the hands and feet.

Today, thanks to more and more research there are specialized products that can be applied safely and effectively at home. There are soothing balms, hydrating lotions for severely dry skin (can also be used for eczema or psoriasis) and cooler rolls and pads for skin experiencing burns or radiation dermatitis.

top tips

TOP TIPS FOR EVERYDAY SKIN AND NAIL CARE

- Use only lukewarm water and a mild soap/body wash when you shower or bath.
- Avoid extremes of heat or cold, including hot baths.
- Avoid hygiene products with alcohol.
- Apply water based creams after the shower while your skin is still damp.
- Do not rub your skin, be gentle and pat it dry after the bath or shower.
- Do not year tight clothing near the treatment area.
- Avoid using perfumes.
- Ask your spouse or loved one to apply lotions too hard to reach areas.
- Drink plenty of liquids every day (aim for 6 glasses of water)
- Speak to your Doctor before you use a skin product to be sure that the ingredients will not cause further irritation.
- Wear a sunscreen of at least SPF 30 to protect your skin at all times
- If your nails become brittle, wear gloves when washing the dishes or doing house work or gardening.
- If you go for a professional manicure bring your own implements to reduce your risk of infection.
- Avoid wearing wraps or acrylic nails, they can trap bacteria,causing infection.
- Ask your manicurist to push back the cuticles, but do not cut them
- Avoid using an acetone based nail polish remover.
- Practice good nail hygiene for toenails

too! Keep the toe nails short and clean and speak to your doctor if notice any signs of infection such as Athletes foot

-
- Today, thanks to organisations here in Ireland there are specific programmes and support groups around the country designed to help those on the road to recovery. As you heal you will look and feel increasingly better if you follow some simple guidelines:
-
- Do not give up your routine grooming activities (wear make-up, fix your hair even if you are confined to bed)
- Consider purchasing a wig or scarf for hair loss.
- Keep up with your dental hygiene.
- If you have lost or gained weight make adjustments to your wardrobe.
- Pamper yourself when you feel well enough (Light touch massage, a facial some reflexology). Be sure to choose a therapist who is qualified in these areas.
- Try to fit in some kind of physical exercise on a daily basis (if you feel up to it and your doctor permits) Something like yoga, palates or ti chi can be gentle on the body, share your current circumstances with your instructor, so that your movements are right for you and your stage of recovery.
- Finally, do not get discouraged – it's normal to have good days and bad days and with sufficient rest and healthy food choices you may look and feel better than ever before!!!!

Christine Clinton, Uisce Day Spa
www.isss.ie

Recommended skin and nail products

La Roche-Posay is a dermatological brand sold exclusively in pharmacies, renowned for its daily routine skincare and make-up products suitable for even the most sensitive skin. Recommended by over 25,000 dermatologists worldwide, La Roche-Posay formulas are created and tested according to thorough pharmaceutical laboratory standards which guarantee maximum efficacy and safety for all skin types. All their formulations are hypoallergenic, non-comedogenic and tested on sensitive skin. They come highly recommended by The Marie Keating Foundation for use during and after cancer treatment. La Roche-Posay is a small town in France which offers dermatological athermalism cures with its unique water. Sourced from a spring in the centre of La Roche-Posay, this thermal water has a unique composition renowned for its dermatological efficacy. Rich in anti-oxidant selenium, La Roche-Posay thermal spring water has soothing, repairing and softening properties and is found in every La Roche-Posay product. Each year, the thermal centre treats over 8,000 adults and children suffering from skin difficulties with skin healing or eczema.

Skincare

Toleriane Dermo Cleanser- Specially formulated for sensitive and reactive skin, its milky texture helps gently cleanse the skin while removing make-up. Its high tolerance formula respects the skin's natural pH.

Toleriane Monodose eye make-up remover is packaged in single-use sterilized doses to ensure and tolerance for even the most sensitive eyes. Its water-like texture instantly soothes and decongests the eyes, leaving a fresh feeling.

Toner

Exceptionally rich in anti-oxidant Selenium, La Roche-Posay Thermal Spring Water has natural soothing, softening and anti-irritating properties. It leaves the skin fresh and ready to moisturise.

Moisturiser

Toleriane Rich helps soothe and protect even the most sensitive, dry and intolerant skin. Only 14 ingredients go into this high-tolerance formula including 7% Shea butter to nourish and protect the skin.

Suncare

It is important to include a high factor sun protection in your daily skincare routine. La Roche-Posay offers a wide range of sun care products including Anthelios Extreme Fluid SPF 50+ for the face, ideal to use alongside your daily moisturiser and before applying your make-up. It provides protection from the sun's UVA+UVB rays that can cause various types of skin damage including skin cancer.

Foundation

Toleriane Foundation is a high coverage semi-matte finish foundation specially formulated for sensitive to intolerant skin. Containing less then 18 ingredients the foundation provides an ultra-fine texture that is preservative free, non-comedogenic, non-acnegenic, non-greasy and oil-free.

Correctors

Toleriane corrector concealer brushes are formulated for even those with the most intolerant skin and target localised imperfections.

La Roche-Posay also offers a maximum coverage concealer with 50% pigments Unifiance Touch Pro for localised or accentuated skin imperfections such as scars.

Mascara

La Roche Posay's Respectissime mascaras are specially formulated to respect the physiology of eyes. For the first time, patented Reconstituted Lachrymal Liquid is used in mascaras – an exact

replica of the eye's natural fluid, it guarantees perfect affinity with sensitive eyes for optimal ocular comfort. RESPECTISSIME DEFINITION helps define and shape the lashes for an anti-flaking hold.

Lips

NOVALIP offers a lipstick range formulated for the most sensitive lips, without compromising on the pleasure of textures and colours.The range includes NOVALIP ROUGE SATIN that contains a gentle micro-exfoliating agent to stimulate cell regeneration which smoothes the lips' surface and improves hold and colour homogeneity. NOVALIP HYRDRASHINE is also available to moisturise the lips with intense shine in 6 glittering shades.

Nails

SILICIUM IS a nail care range formulated with silicium-diffusion technology to fortify and restore soft and weakened nails. Pastel Care, available in 3 shades, helps strengthen fragile nails. After 2 weeks of use nails regain a healthy and natural appearance. Color Bloc offers 7 anti-shock colours. Pro Manicure ensures healthy nail and cuticles with a long lasting manicure effect with 3 different expert actions.

www.laroche-posay.ie

61

EYEBROW & EYELASH CARE

Losing some or all of your eyebrows and eyelashes from chemotherapy can be difficult. Whether you have lost all your brows and lashes or you are at the stage when your hair is growing back, there are some simple makeup techniques to help you overcome this.

Eyebrows

Sometimes eyebrow hair can grow back differently to what you had previously - the hair may be coarser and the shape/colour of the eyebrows may change.

- If you have no eyebrows, you need to feel for the shape of the brow bone first. Find your brow bone by running your finger on the top of the bony area over your eye. This is your guide to where your brow should be.
- Follow the techniques in the Eyebrow section to find the three points to recreate the shape and use a pencil to dot them.
- Connect the dots using very light, short strokes with a sharpened pencil to give the

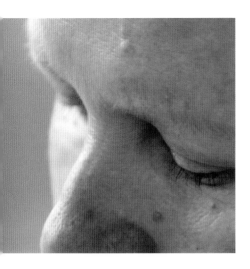

illusion of short hairs

- Using an angled eyebrow brush apply some eyebrow powder over the pencil in the same way to set it and prevent it from smudging
- Step back & look in a mirror to make sure both eyebrows are even & natural looking
- Check with your doctor before waxing or dyeing your brows.

Eyelashes

- Eyelashes can grow back thicker, thinner or sparse in some areas.
- To create a lash line apply a dark eye shadow on the lash line and then smudge upwards with a cotton bud
- Use a kohl pencil to apply eyeliner to the inner rims of the upper lids – this instantly gives strength to the lash line without looking heavy on top
- For sparse lashes underneath the eyes smudge a little eye shadow under the eyes to create a shadow and the illusion of lashes
- If you have no lashes try using strip lashes with an invisible band, that are not too thick or long and are black in colour
- Use individual lashes to fill in missing or sparse lashes See Luscious Lashes Section for more details on applying false lashes

Rhona Cullinan
www.professionalmakeup.ie

HAIR & WIG CARE

Losing some or all of your hair from cancer treatment or even alopecia can be traumatic but thankfully today there is a wide range of wigs and hair accessories to help you through this time. Here are some useful tips and advice for choosing and maintaining your wig and for looking after your hair during regrowth.

Choosing and wearing your wig

- Have your wig fitted before you lose your hair so wig fitter can see texture, density, style and colour of your natural hair.
- Make sure you are putting your wig on correctly with the front rim of the wig on or above your original hairline; never below as this makes it look like your hair is growing out of your forehead. Many women do this because they are afraid that the wig will blow off. It won't. Remember the size of the wig can adjusted at the back.
- If your wig is irritating your scalp, line it with white gauze bandage. Steep it in tea first to give it a skin colour. This bandage is hypo-allergenic and absorbs sweat so it can be used like a sweat band also.

Making you wig look more natural

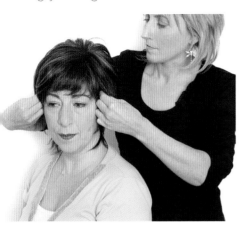

- Get it thinned out if it looks too full.
- Feather cut fringe and locks to give the illusion that the wig is less dense if your natural hair is fine.
- Wigs with highlights often look less dense and therefore more natural
- Styling your wig into your own shape with all its little quirks can really personalise it and make it feel like your own.
- Breaking up the wig hair with your fingers or with product (gloss or wax) will give it a more natural or textured look
- Bringing some hair behind the ears will make it look more natural especially if wig appears too full around the face but leave some hair in front of your ears as your locks.
- Use a scarf or hair accessories to decorate the wig.
- If your head looks a bit flat when wearing headwear, put a shoulder pad on the crown of your head underneath.

A change from the wig

There is a good variety of headwear specially designed for people with hair loss so that they cover the full head. These are a nice break from the wig and are cooler to wear. A fringe piece can be attached to the front of these to take the bare look away.

On the other hand, if you really want to wear your regular baseball caps or bandanas that do not cover the full head at the back, you can get hair that looks like a halo of hair and hangs beneath your own regular hats. These are also cooler to wear than wigs.

Care of re-growth hair after treatment

- Hair grows at approx half an inch per month. If the re-growth is fine downy hair, it is advisable to have the tips trimmed off.
- Do not colour your hair with permanent colour for 6 months after your treatment. Colour that has no ammonia or peroxide can be used. These colours wash out after 6 washes. Try out some coloured mousses too.
- There isn't anything proven that you can do to speed up your hair re-growth but wearing a wig will not hinder it.
- Try a volumising shampoo and conditioner.

top tips

TOP TIPS FOR HAIR AND SCALP CARE DURING TREATMENT

- Use a mild shampoo and conditioner.
- Use a low heat on the hairdryer if at all
- Do not colour your hair with permanent colour
- Try to limit the amount you wash and style your hair
- Use a soft brush
- If you've lost your hair and your scalp is dry, use a good moisturiser for sensitive skin

Anne Roche, Roches Hair Solutions
www.hair4u.ie

65

THE
MAKEOVERS

4

" I was always eager to use real women instead of models in the book. Seeing the difference that makeup can make, the smile in their eyes and the reaction when they look in the mirror is a very gratifying experience. When we decided to write the makeover book for charity the decision about models was not a question. I wanted to use real women that other women reading the book could relate to.

I was lucky to have met a lot of amazing people over the years: **Sue** who's remarkable personality and positive attitude makes it hard for me to believe the amount of cancer treatment she has been going through over the last few years. **Katie** who has experienced tragic times over recent years and who is now herself helping other families to deal with the unbearable pain of losing a child. Hannah born with a cleft palette lip. **Kerri**, a teenager who sufferers from severe acne of the back and face causing her to become withdrawn, shy and lacking in confidence. **Caroline**, a true survivor who having been diagnosed with cancer at the same time as her mother battled through the disease and now embarks on a new life and a new look. **Frankie**, a beautiful young lady suffering from a condition we usually associate with women at least twice her age or more – arthritis.

Six truly inspirational women who despite all their difficulties prove the essence of this book - if you look good, you can feel good "

Rhona

lucky ones and she died in 2004. I married my lovely husband John on the 1st of July 2005. His father died of a massive heart attack at the wedding! A wedding no one will forget even if it is for the wrong reason! 14 weeks after we married I found a lump in my breast while having a shower. It was a Saturday evening. I had no hesitation in deciding to go to the doctor and was in his surgery first thing on Monday morning.

He thought it was a cyst and put me on anti-biotics. After a week or so there was no change in the lump and so I was referred to St. James's Hospital. I had a mamogram, an ultra sound and an aspiration. Abnormal cells were found and so I had a lumpectomy. A few days later I was told I had cancer and the following week I had a partial mastectomy and some lymph nodes removed.

About 6 weeks after that I started chemotherapy in St. James's Hospital and

M y name is Susan but everyone calls me Sue (unless they're annoyed with me!). I'm 42 years young. My first real contact with someone who had breast cancer was when my sister-in law was diagnosed in 2002. Unfortunately Bettie was not one of the

> **When you're bald and have no eyebrows or eyelashes, it's very hard to feel feminine**

and traumatic things. Hair is a huge part of a person's identity. "She's blonde". "She's brunette". "She has short spiky hair". "She has long black hair". If you describe someone, hair's one of the first things you talk about. When you're bald and have no eye brows or eye lashes, it's very hard to feel feminine. You lose a major part of yourself. That's where wigs and makeup come in. They make such a huge difference to your confidence.

Unfortunately I was rediagnosed with cancer in February 2007. I've been receiving chemotherapy treatment 3 out of every 4 weeks for the last year. I have lost a lot of my hair again including my eye lashes and eye brows. My skin tone has changed and it has become very dry. I also have a lot of spots which I never had before.

when I finished the chemotherapy treatment I then had 33 sessions of radiotherapy in St. Lukes Hospital. I lost all my hair due to the chemo and I put on over a stone because of the steroids I had to take and the lack of exercise due to sickness. I had been a very active person with a job that required lots of energy.

I had to take nearly a year off work. Losing my hair was probably one of the most stressful

When Rhona thought me how to put on my make-up including putting on false eye lashes and 'drawing' on my brows, it made such a huge difference to me especially when I have my wig on as well. Confident and feminine.

Suddenly I'm not the person with cancer, I'm just Sue!

71

Step 1
Sue has been suffering with a lot of blemishes due to treatment she has received. After applying a moisturiser, I used a corrective concealer to reduce the redness on her face. For foundation I used a creamy texture as she suffers from dry skin. For the eyes I began by applying a base colour, then a medium brown eye shadow on lid & blended away the edges.

Step 2
Sue has lost a lot of her lashes due to chemotherapy so to thicken the lash line I applied a thin layer of gel eyeliner to the base of the lashes.

Step 3
Using a tweezers I applied a set of natural strip lashes close to the lash line and applied mascara to blend them in.

Step 4
To give Sue some more definition to her weakened eyebrows I used a sharpened eye brow pencil to draw in the missing brows

Step 5
To make the brow colour last longer, I used an eyebrow powder to set the pencil using short strokes to replicate hairs.

Step 6
To define her lower lash line I applied some brown eye shadow under her eyes and blended the excess with a cotton bud.

Step 7
After applying some blusher to the apples of the cheeks I then applied some lip liner and lipstick to finish the makeup.

Step 8
We completed the look by choosing and fitting a suitable wig for Sue to give her back her femininity.

Sue before:

products used

Moisturiser	La Roche Posay Nutritic 5%
Concealer	La Roche Posay Unifiance Pro Corrector Pencil
Foundation	La Roche Posay Satin Cream
Eye Shadows	Mac Vanilla (base colour)
	Mac Patina
Mascara	La Roche Posay Densifier Black
Gel Liner	Mac Fluidline Blacktrack
Eye Lashes	Ardell Strip Lashes
Eyebrow Pencil	Mac Coffee
Eyebrow Powder	Laura Mercier Brow Duo – Rich Brown
Blush	Dr Hauschka Stone Colours Collection
Lipliner	Mac Spice
Lipstick	La Roche Posay Novalip 170

Sue after:

"Confident and feminine. Suddenly I'm not the person with cancer, I'm just Sue!"

KATES STORY

My name is Kate, I'm 47, married to Karl for 17 years. We had 3 beautiful children. Had Kieran lived he would have been 10 this year. Over the years I had several late miscarriages and up until Kieran was diagnosed we thought that was the worst thing that could possibly happen to us. After our last miscarriage we felt we just couldn't do this any more. It was too much pain. We had three beautiful healthy children (though Kieran had a few medical problems over the years) which was a greater blessing than many ever have and decided to just get on with our lives enjoy what we had.

Then in 2002 on Kieran's 4th birthday, he was diagnosed with Myloid Dysplastic Syndrome, a very rare and difficult form of cancer to treat. His chances weren't good and his only hope was a bone marrow transplant which was scheduled for the following January. Before that though he had to have two blocks of very aggressive chemo and then a week of 'conditioning' (a very misleading description of the BMT preparation) where bone marrow was quite literally wiped out completely, then transplant. Life was horrendous; our whole world was turned upside down. His treatment was horrific which any one who has undergone chemo will understand. I would have sold my soul to take his place. To watch your child suffer like that felt at times beyond endurance. He was the most amazing little boy and like nearly all the kids in St John's, accepted the pain, and

> **We had already been told there was no other treatment possible. I'd have sold my soul to take his place**

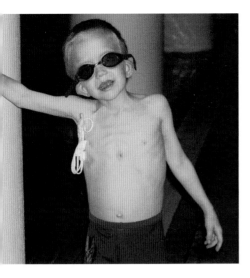

told me that he didn't want to die but he wasn't afraid, but this day he was alive and he was going to enjoy it. For us that was like saying when I'm gone I know its going to hurt but you have to make the most of every day and that is what we've tried to do.

Two ago we were blessed with the arrival of David. When I realised I was pregnant I was completely shocked. I felt between my age and history everything was against it, but the boys believed this was a gift from Kieran. David has brought a sense of joy back to our family that we never thought we'd have again. I've realised that while the pain of Kieran's death will never leave me, that your life can grow around it and

horror of the treatment with unbelievable grace. All three boys amazed us by their courage throughout. Ian and Kevin hated seeing him sick, and missed him so much when he was in hospital but they all accepted that this was now it had to be. Initially he did really well after transplant and we thought we could see that glimmer of hope, but just days before his 5th birthday, he relapsed. We had already been told that there was no other treatment possible if this happened so straight away we realised that it was now a matter of time. The hospital were brilliant and encouraged us to throw all the 'transplant rules' out the window and really live his last few months and by god we did. We got 6 more very precious months with him. He died at home, in our arms on the 31st January 2004 - he was exactly 5 and half years old.

Life since, has been very hard. Sometimes especially in the early days you practically had to claw your way out of bed, but we had two other young boys who were very much alive, and also suffering hugely and we needed to get our lives together for them. Kieran has been our inspiration throughout both his illness and since his death. He fought so hard to live right to the end. Even to the point that when he knew he was dying (we never told him, he told us) he

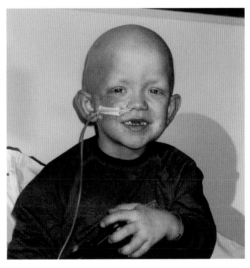

there are many blessings ahead of me. In time you learn to live with the pain and accept it as part of your life. Joy and sorrow are two sides of the same coin.

About a year and a half after Kieran died, we set up Anam Cara (**www.anamcara.ie**) which is a peer support group for bereaved parents and siblings. Our aim is to reach out to families who have experienced a similar loss and hopefully give them some hope, comfort, understanding and encouragement throughout their future lives.

Step 1

To begin Katie's make over I applied a moisturising primer to her face. Using the rounded foundation brush I applied a creamy foundation and blended well.

Step 2

Katie suffers from puffy areas under the eyes. Mixing a little highlight concealer with the foundation I applied it to the darker line under the puffy area – this brightens up the dark area making the puffiness less obvious.

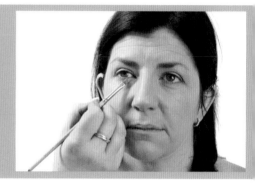

Step 3

After applying a cream coloured base from the eyelids to the eyebrows I then used a warm brown tone on the lids bringing it slightly outwards over the socket line to reduce the heavy brow area. .

Step 4

Using a blending eye shadow brush I used circular motions to blend away the obvious line left by the eye shadow. The brown eye shadow should fade into the cream base making it more subtle.

Step 5

After applying a very thin layer of eyeliner to the upper lids to enhance the lash line I then applied some eye pencil to the lower lids and blended the excess away with a cotton bud.

Step 6

I then applied black mascara to the upper and lower lashes and groomed her eyebrows into shape.

Step 7

To warm up Kate's complexion and give her an instant glow I applied some blusher to the apples of the cheeks and blended away any excess with the foundation brush.

Step 8

To complete Kate's transformation I lined her lips and applied lipstick

Kate before:

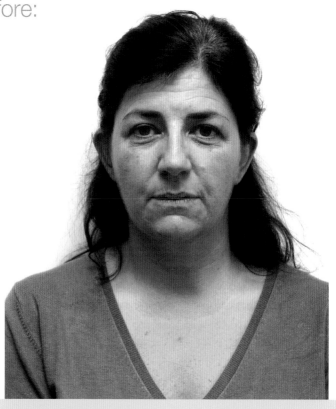

products used

Moisturiser	Estee Lauder Perfectionist
Concealer	YSL Touche Eclat
Foundation	Estee Lauder Futurist
Eye Shadows	Estee Lauder Pure Colour – Ivory Box
	Estee Lauder Pure Colour – Copper Penny
Mascara	L'Oreal Double Extend Beauty Tubes - black
Gel Liner	Mac Fluidline Blacktrack
Eye Pencil	MAC Eye Pencil Coffee
Blush	Estee Lauder Rosewood
Lipliner	Laura Mercier
Lipstick	Laura Mercier Maple
Hair	Coloured and Styled by Susan Peggs

Kate after:

" I've realised that while the pain of Kieran's death will never leave me, life can grow around it. Kieran has been our inspiration "

HANNAHS STORY

With the lip it's the same, it doesn't fully fuse together when the baby is being developed during pregnancy which results in the slight scar on the lip from being surgically sewn together.

Growing up I never really noticed it I was too busy obsessed with Barbies! But when I started going to secondary school I became a lot more self conscious and a simple thing like talking to boys became this huge task. For a good while I went very into myself and quiet because I felt rather self conscious often thinking I was quite the ugly duckling but now I have come to terms with it and accepted that that's just me and you can't change that. I never actually knew that I could correct my lip with make up and it was really interesting to see how it could be done. It was strange looking at myself for the first time

Hi my name is Hannah Mc Cabe, I'm 17 years old and I was born with a cleft pallet and lip. What that basically means is that the roof of the mouth doesn't fully form and there is a gap on the pallet of the mouth.

> " I felt like an ugly duckling and it felt quite strange when I first saw myself without the scar. Now I've one less thing to worry about! "

without my scar and it took me a while to get used to it but I felt like a new person and had a new found confidence in myself. It has taken me a while to perfect doing it on myself but now that I have, I feel more confident and have

one less thing to worry about when I'm heading on a night.

I would like to thank Rhona so much for showing me how to do this and giving me a confidence boost! Thank you.

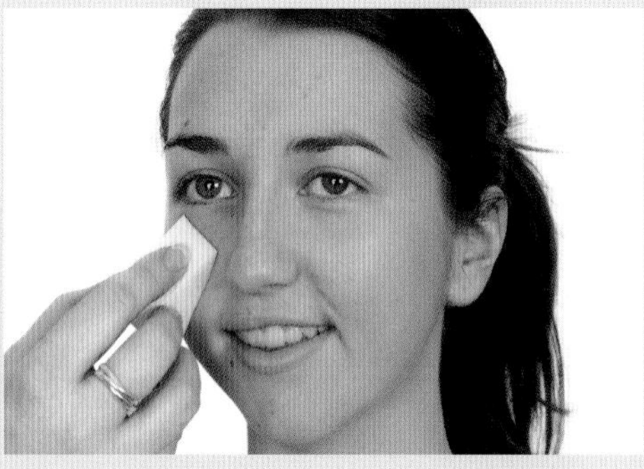

Step 1
Hannah has great skin so I used a tinted moisturiser with a sponge just to even out her skin tones and blended it well

Step 2
To bring out her eyes I began with a cream base all over the lid and then applied a light brown to her eyelids

Step 3
I applied a darker shadow to define her socket line making sure to blend away any hard edges

Step 4
After applying a thin layer of eyeliner to the upper lashes I then applied Mascara to both her upper and lower lashes. Bending the wand helped to get the mascara right to the roots giving her more volume

Step 5

As Hannah is quite young I used a soft blush to the apples of the cheeks to give her a fresh look

Step 6

To correct Hannah's lip shape I began by using a lip liner corrector pencil to outline just outside where the natural lip line should be, recreating a new lip shape

Step 7

Using this new line as a guide I applied a coloured lip pencil just under this line.

Step 8

I filled in the lips with lipstick and used a pointed cotton bud to blend away the excess corrector pencil to finish the look

Hannah before:

products used

Foundation	Benefit Tinted Moisturiser
Eye Shadows	Rimmel Colour Rush Eye Quad – Smokey Brun
Mascara	L'Oreal Beauty Tubes
Gel Liner	Smashbox – Gel Liner Black
Blush	Rimmel Blusher Pink Rose
Corrector Pencil	Makeup Forever Lip Corrector
Lipliner	Mac Spice
Lipstick	Rimmel Heather Shimmer

Hannah after:

"I never knew I could correct my lip shape with makeup, I feel like a new person!"

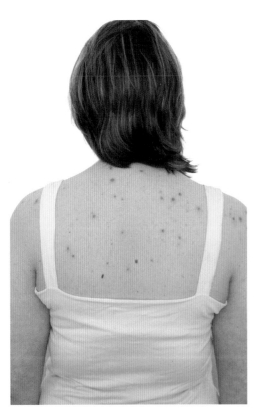

My name is Kerri Ward, I'm seventeen, and like all teenage girls I've always fretted about my skin. From about fourteen I suffered with acne on my face, back and chest. Though it started out inconspicuous enough, it quickly developed into a problem. To attempt to cover it I applied thick concealer and foundation, which only made it worse. I desperately tried every cleanser, Exfoliator, herbal cure and medication I could find – it was no use. Even when the spots and swelling went away temporarily, I was still left with embarrassing scars.

> When I see pictures of myself as a child, I can't help feeling depressed.

I was ashamed of my skin, and started dressing in dark, baggy clothes and keeping my hair long

to cover my face. I was bullied in school. When my friends started going out more, socialising and dating, I did everything I could to become invisible. It was even worse during the summer months. I didn't have the confidence to wear a swimsuit, because at times my acne spread to my arms and flared up on my neck, and I covered up completely even on the hottest days. When friends went to the beach, I stayed in. Though I had once been a bubbly and outgoing person, I became withdrawn, quiet and depressed. It may seem to many as a minor, even trivial issue, but it was enough to make me miserable.

As I came to the end of my sixth year in school, I knew it would only be a few months to my debs – and I was dreading it. It would mean having to wear a revealing dress and having to show my acne. I couldn't bear the thought of it. I wanted to be able to look forward to celebrating the end of my school life, instead of having to worry about my appearance, as always. One night of freedom from my haunting self-consciousness didn't seem too much to ask. When I met Rhona, she showed how to properly apply make-up to best cover my spots without aggravating my skin. She told me which products to use to minimise my spots and scarring, and gave me a regime to follow. The results were astonishing; when I looked in the mirror I couldn't believe it was me. Though I still had spots, wearing the correct make-up allowed me, just for a little while, to see myself without that shadow of insecurity – and I loved what I saw. By the end of the day, I couldn't wait for the debs – and the look of surprise on everyone's faces when I arrived!

Though I still have spots, and make-up is only a temporary solution, getting the chance to see myself without them, as a normal teenage girl, liberated me from my self-consciousness. I still worry about them, of course, but now I can go out with my friends and relax on the beach without worrying about them so much. I even have a boyfriend now to take me to my debs!

89

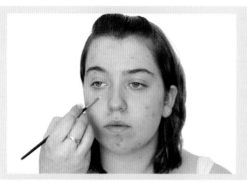

Step 1
To reduce the redness and spots on Kerri's face and back I used a small concealer brush to apply a yellow concealer to those areas.

Step 2
With a clean cotton bud I then blended around the edges leaving the concealer only on the blemishes .

Step 3
Then I applied a skin corrective foundation to the skin blending carefully. Using a large powder brush I dusted some translucent powder to her face to set the foundation and concealer.

Step 4
To bring out Kerri's lovely eyes I used a white eye shadow from the lid to the brows as a base. Then I used a medium colour from the lid to the socket line to create a light smokey look and blended the edges with a blending brush.

Step 5
After applying a little shimmer powder to her lids I then re highlighted her brow bone with some shimmery white eye shadow.

Step 6
As Kerri is so young and is used to wearing a lot of makeup I applied a thick line of eyeliner to her upper lids and coated her lashes with mascara. I brushed her eyebrows into shape with an eyebrow comb.

Step 7
Using a powder blusher I applied it to her cheeks sweeping upwards towards the hairline to add some shape to her cheekbones.

Step 8
To keep the focus on Kerri's eyes, I just used a lightly coloured gloss to her lips to finish her look..

Kerri before:

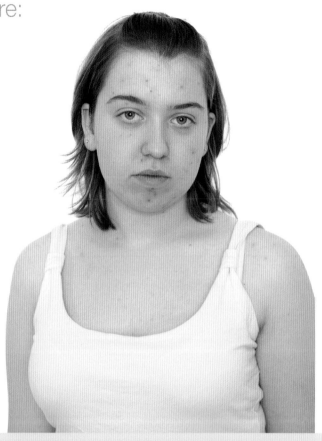

products used

Concealer	La Roche Posay Unifiance Pro Corrector Pencil - yellow
Foundation	La Roche Posay Unifiance Corrective Film
Powder	Dr Hauschka Translucent Powder
Eye Shadows	Base Colour Mac Vanilla
	Mac Tempting
	Shimmer Mac Pigment Copper Sparkle
	Highlighter Mac Pigment Vanilla
Gel Liner	Shiseido Eyeliner Black
Mascara	La Roche Posay Duo Scopic Mascara
Blush	Rimmel Smoked Oyster
Lipstick	L'Oreal Glam 6 Hour Glam Shine Hold on Rose

Kerri after:

When I looked in
the mirror I couldn't
believe it was me!

things. I was feeling very tired and drained for about six months, my stomach became very bloated. I would feel very full even if I only ate small amounts of food. I was getting regular kidney infections and bad back pain and also bad pain in my left side. I just put it down to "women's problems". When I decided to go to my GP, he suggested I go for an abdominal scan. I went three days later for the scan in St. James hospital and was told that I had a huge cyst on my left ovary, 9cm in size. A week later I had an appointment with a gynaecologist and after various blood tests she confirmed that my cyst was cancerous and quite an aggressive tumour for someone of my age.

> " Now I can tell people who are diagnosed with cancer that there is light at the end of the tunnel and you can beat it. "

Hi my name is Caroline. I'm 37 years old and live with my partner Ken and Daughter Amy. I live in Crumlin now and work locally but I am originally from Terenure where my mother, father and brothers still live. I was diagnosed with ovarian cancer just after my 36th birthday.

It was quite a shock to be told I had cancer as I didn't look or really feel that sick - in fact everyone was saying I looked very well as I had just returned from a Mediterranean cruise. When I think back though there certainly were tell tale signs but I put that down to other

On the 31st of August 2006 I had a full hysterectomy. After the operation I was laid up for about 7 days and had tubes coming out of every part of me. I was relieved to hear that they got all the cancer and that it was at stage 1 and hadn't spread any place else, but as a precaution I would need to have chemotherapy. I think that actually bothered me more than the actual operation itself - not only had I lost my ovaries and womb but now I was going to lose my hair and eyelashes. I always took pride in

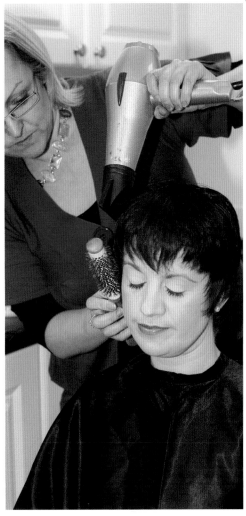

myself and was one of these people who didn't like to go out without having their hair looking half decent and the war paint on! It was also at this time that my mother was diagnosed with breast cancer so things really couldn't get much worse!! While I was at home recovering, my mother went in to St. Vincent's hospital and had a lump removed from her breast. Thankfully was also at very early stages.

Chemo started for me on the 26th September 2006. I had four lots of it and was finished by Christmas 2006. I had two nice wigs, a long blonde one styled very similar to my own hair and a short blonde wig for when I felt like a change. The chemo wasn't too bad for me. I had a few days when I was completely knocked out from it but overall it wasn't as bad as I thought it would be. I was still able to get out and about and meet friends for lunch and do most normal things I just had to be careful not to catch a cold or flu because your immune system is so low from all the stuff they pump into you. My mother started her chemo after Christmas. In a way we weren't too scared about what was happening because we were going through the same thing at the same time. If either one felt down or sick we knew it wasn't

going to last and that each time we got our chemo we were also one step nearer the finish line. Some day life would be back to normal. It's now 18 months since I was given the all clear - my hair is back but in a different shorter style and I've returned to work. My mam is over it too and her hair is back.

Thank God we are both so lucky to come through it so well and maybe help other people who are worried or scared after being diagnosed with cancer. There can be light at the end of the tunnel and you can beat it!

Step 1
Since Caroline hadn't touched her eyebrows since they grew back I began by plucking them into shape and used a similar coloured eye shadow to fill in any gaps.

Step 2
After applying a primer I used a flat foundation brush I blended on a light layer of foundation to even out her skin tones. Her skin is blemish free so I didn't need to use concealer.

Step 3
To keep her eyes quite natural I used a soft matt colour on her lids to brighten and open up her eyes.

Step 4
To enhance her lash line without looking heavy I applied some brown eye shadow to the roots of her upper lashes and blended gently with a cotton bud.

Step 5
To open up Caroline's eyes even more I used a white pencil to line the inner rim of her lower lash line. This makes the white of the eyes look even whiter.

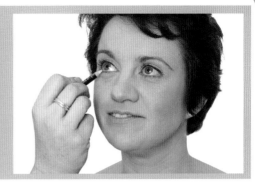

Step 6
I used a lash defining brown mascara to coat her upper and lower lashes.

Step 7
Caroline likes a more natural look so to avoid the use of powder I used a cream blush to add some colour to her cheeks using my fingers to blend it.

Step 8
To complete the look I used a coloured lip gloss to define her lips.

Caroline before:

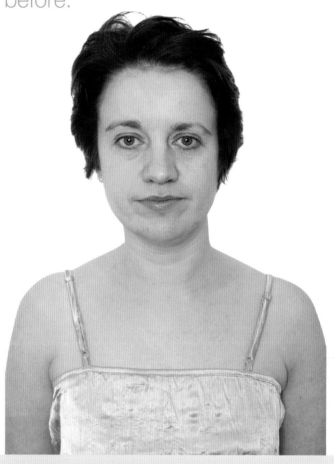

Primer	NO 7 Protect and Perfect
Foundation	Dr Hauschka Foundation
Eye shadows	MAC Bamboo
	MAC Ground Brown
Mascara	La Roche Posay Definition Mascara Brown
Eye Pencil	Makeup Forever White Eye Pencil
Blush	Bobbi Brown Cream Blush Stick Coral
Lipgloss	MAC Lip Glass Lychee Luxe

Caroline after:

"
With my new hair
and a new look,
I now feel like a new
version of the old
me! "

Arthritis has led me on a hard journey from the age of four. From missing out on activities at school because of hospital trips to missing days off work because of severe pain and stiffness it has been a difficult road to travel. At the age of 17 I started to balloon from taking regular steroid that masked the symptoms of arthritis including swelling of my joints. I went from a size 8 to a size 18 and as my size grew my self esteem shrank. At 18 I decided to ditch the steroids and embark on a new road, one that I controlled. I lost the weight, started on a homeopathic diet and reached deep into myself to find outwho I was regardless of arthritis.

In 2005 I started having a few photo shoots in England. It then progressed to Germany and Ireland where I now live. Being in front of the

camera boosts my self-esteem but I couldn't do it without make-up! When I am feeling bad and down in the dumps make-up always gives me the lift and the confidence boost I need, whether I am having a photoshoot or going to town.

> **When I'm in pain and feeling down in the dumps, I know that makeup will give me a lift to boost my self confidence**

I would love to be a model full-time but no amount of make-up will take away my arthritis and make me walk without a limp down the catwalk or fix my deformed hand which has been eroded, but it doesn't matter.
I have been fairly successful given my condition but above that I now have the confidence to know that my arthritis can't and won't hold me back!

Step 1

Starting on the eyes first, I applied a light layer of foundation to the lids and set it with a dusting of translucent powder. I then applied white eye shadow to the entire lid as a base.

Step 2

Using a flat eye shadow brush I applied a dark shade from the lashes up and a little over the socket line.

Step 3

With a blending brush I used small circles over and back to blend the eye shadow into the white base at the socket line. Take care not to go near the eye shadow on the lid as for smokey eyes this should be kept as a solid colour

Step 4

To enhance the lid I applied some pigment which will make the colour more intense, bringing out her gorgeous eyes

Step 5

To clean up the eyes I used a makeup cleansing wipe to remove all the excess makeup under her eyes leaving it fresh for a clean foundation

Step 6

To really define her lash lines I applied an eye liner pencil to the upper and lower "inside" rim of her eyes. Lining the rims of the upper eye area takes practice and care.

Step 7

I added some black eye shadow under her bottom lashes to both set the eye liner and to deepen the intensity of the colour. To give her eyes a smokier look, I pressed a small amount of the pigment over the black eye shadow and used a cotton bud to smudge and blend it

Step 8

To complete the look, I tidied her eyebrows, applied mascara, foundation, highlighter and a light dusting of blusher and kept her lips to a nude gloss.

Frankie before:

products used

Foundation	Mac Studio Fix
Eye Shadows	Mac Maylar (base colour)
	Mac Tempting
	Mac Pigment Rich
Mascara	La Roche Posay – Duoscopic Black
Gel Liner	Mac Fluid line Blacktrack
Eyebrow Pencil	Mac Ebony
Blush	MAC Pinch Me
Lip Gloss	Face 2 Mocha Mist

Frankie after:

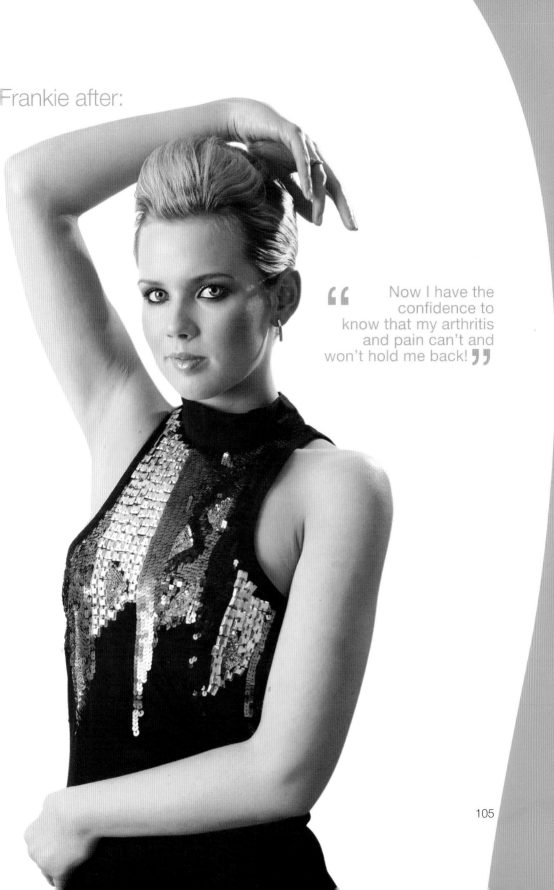

" Now I have the
confidence to
know that my arthritis
and pain can't and
won't hold me back! "

About the authors

RHONA CULLINAN

Rhona Cullinan (IBPA Professional Makeup Artist of the Year 2008) is one of Irelands leading Freelance Makeup Artists. Over the last 15 years she has worked with many celebrities and Cosmetic Brands and has gained extensive experience in all areas of the industry including Fashion, Beauty, Photography, Editorial, Catwalk, Television and Bridal Makeup. Rhona is also a director of The Powder Room Girls, Irelands leading agency for freelance hair and makeup artists.
www.professionalmakeup.ie
www.prg.ie

DEREK O'KELLY

Derek O' Kelly is director at The Irish Academy of Beauty, Irelands leading provider of training for beauty therapists and make up artists. He has spent the past 18 years developing and delivering educational programmes for beauty, makeup, massage, fitness, business, personal development and teaching. Derek spends much of his time writing content for his companies websites and is currently working on a self help book for adults returning to education.
www.academy.ie
www.beautycourses.ie

Contributors

PHOTOGRAPHY BY BETA BAJGARTOVA

Beta came from Czech Republic to live in Dublin in 2004. Last couple of years she has been working as a principal in-house photographer for VIP magazine, Kiss and TVnow magazines. She did dozens excellent photo shoots with numerous celebrities such as Westlife, Gerry Ryan, Kathryn Thomas, Calum Best, Blathnaid Ni Cofaigh, Marry Kennedy, Daniell O'Donnell, Kevin Myers, Grainne and Sile Seoiges, Cecilia Ahern and many others. While working for teenage Kiss magazine she also proved herself as a very talented fashion photographer. Beta is also very busy wedding photographer. In recent years she did photograph numerous weddings in Ireland and abroad and her happy clients are assured to testify that she is discreet, sensible and furthermore reliable and enjoyable photographer who delivers beautiful shots from the wedding day and supplies stunning albums

To contact Beta call 087 2770063 or log onto www.betawedding.com and send an e-mail to beta@betawedding.com.

EDITING AND LAYOUT BY mOuLd DESIGN
mOuLd Design are a Dublin based design group specialising in everything from book design, corporate identity, image making, digital design, web development and everything in between. Email: mouldgraphics@gmail.com

ANN ROCHE – Director of Roche's Hair Solutions – expert advice and services through all stages of hair loss.
www.hair4u.ie

CHRISTINE CLINTON – Director of International Spa and Salon Services and expert in cancer related skin care.
www.isss.ie

SUSAN PEGGS – A Director of The Powder Room Girls and one of Irelands Leading Hair Stylists www.susanpeggs.com

LA ROCHE POSAY – a dermatological skin care and cosmetic brand recommended by top dermatologists for all skin types even the most sensitive.
www.laroche-posay.ie

PHOTO CREDITS
Beta Bajgartova: www.betawedding.com
Morgan Studios: www.morganstudios.ie
Tatiana G: www.tatianag.com

Acknowledgements

To Sue, Hannah, Katie, Caroline, Kerri and Frankie. Thank you so much for your time and for sharing your incredible stories with us. You are an inspiration to us all!

A very special thanks to Beta Bajgartova, an amazing photographer and a wonderful friend. Thank you so much for the time and passion you dedicated to this publication. Your photos truly captured the essence of this book. Without your expertise, advice and support this book would not have been possible.

To Linda Keating and all the team at the Marie Keating Foundation - Thank you for all the support from day one and your guidance in steering the direction of this book. Your dedication, determination and hard work in the battle against breast cancer brings hope and awareness to many.

To all the team at The Irish Academy of Beauty and Makeup especially Veronica, Ray, Breda, Teresa, Natasha and Kathleen – for your support and facilities

To Greg White and all the Cullinan Family for your love, patience and support

To Susan Peggs, an amazing hairdresser and friend

To Valerie Ward, a great makeup artist and friend thanks for all your help and advice

To Gerry Morgan, for all your help and support and doing such a wonderful job of printing this book

To Paul, Mould Design, thank you so much for all the amazing and professional work in creating and designing this book for us.

To Genevieve at The Casting Couch

Photography Studios, Fitzwilliam Square, Dublin, for donating your facilities for the photo shoots.

To everyone who helped raise funds towards the printing costs of this book including:
The students of NUIM Maynooth, especially Greg White and Peter Dunne of the Snooker Club and the Maynooth Gospel Choir, Ken Doherty, The hair and makeup team from The Powder Room Girls and Makeup. And also to thank – Brett Fairholm – Irish Beauty, Dave Horton AIT Insurance, Salon Magazine, Aisling Beirne, Tatiana G, Capital D – RTE, Chaste Creative Productions, Look Good Feel Better, TV3 Expose, St James Hospital Oncology Unit

And everyone else who helped us along the way.

Rhona & Derek

Useful websites

COSMETICS

LA ROCHE POSAY
www.laroche-posay.ie
MAC COSMETICS
www.maccosmetics.com
ESTEE LAUDER
www.esteelauder.com
MAKEUP FOREVER
www.makeupforever.com
BOBBI BROWN COSMETICS
www.bobbibrown.co.uk
NO 7 COSMETICS
www.boots.ie
FACE 2
www.face2.ie
RIMMEL
www.rimmellondon.com
BENEFIT MAKEUP
www.benefitcosmetics.com
LAURA MERCIER
www.lauramercier.com

L'OREAL PARIS
www.loreal-paris.co.uk
SHISEIDO
www.sca.shiseido.com
YVES SAINT LAURENT
www.ysl.com
DR HAUSCHKA
www.drhauschka.ie

OTHER RESOURCES

MARIE KEATING FOUNDATION
www.mariekeating.ie
PREVENTION AND EARLY DETECTION
www.cancer.ie/prevention
CANCER RESEARCH UK
www.cancerhelp.org.uk
LOOK GOOD FEEL BETTER PROGRAM
www.lookgoodfeelbetter.ie
ARTHRITIS IRELAND
www.arthritisireland.ie/
CHILDRENS CHRONIC ARTHRITIS
ASSOCIATION UK
www.arthritiscare.org.uk
CLEFT LIP AND PALATE ASSOCIATION
IRELAND
www.cleft.ie
KATES WEBSITE FOR BEREAVED PARENTS
www.anamcara.ie
LEUKAEMIA – THE FACTS
www.ukccsg.org.uk
CHILDREN WITH LEUKAEMIA
www.leukaemia.org/
SKIN PROBLEMS RESOURCE
www.skinhelp.co.uk
IRISH ACNE INFORMATION CENTRE
www.acne.ie